# Vocabulary
## in Context
### FOR THE COMMON CORE STANDARDS

## Grade
# 7

# Table of Contents

Vocabulary in Context G7, SV 9780547625805

# Introduction

Steck-Vaughn's *Vocabulary in Context* series offers parents and educators high-quality, curriculum-based products that align with the Common Core Standards for English Language Arts for grades 2–9.

Each unit in the *Vocabulary in Context* books includes:

- fiction and/or nonfiction selections, covering a wide variety of topics

- context activities, ascertaining that students understand what they have read

- vocabulary activities, challenging students to show their understanding of key vocabulary

- questions in a standardized-test format, helping prepare students for standardized exams

- word skills activities, targeting additional vocabulary words and vocabulary skills

- writing activities, providing assignments that encourage students to use the vocabulary words

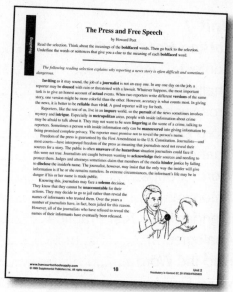

**Reading selection**

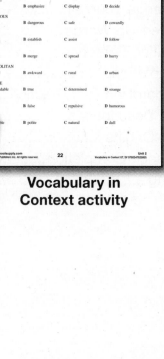

**Vocabulary in Context activity**

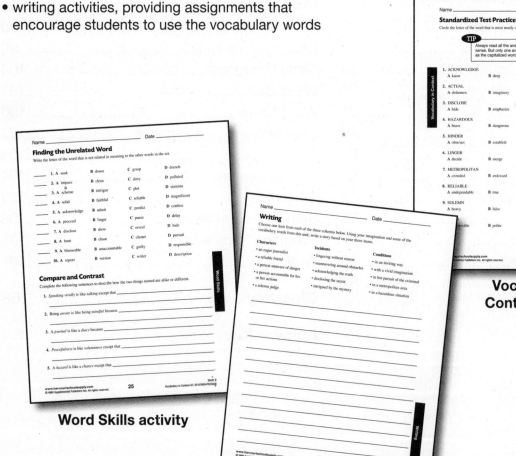

**Word Skills activity**

**Writing activity**

# Determining Meaning Through Word Analysis

Words are made up of various combinations of the following parts: prefix, suffix, base word, and root. Analysis of these parts is another way to determine an unfamiliar word's meaning.

**Prefix**      a word part that is added to the beginning of another word or word part

**Suffix**      a word part that is added to the end of another word or word part

**Base Word**      a complete word to which a prefix and/or a suffix may be added

**Root**      a word part to which a prefix and/or a suffix must be added. A root cannot stand alone.

## Prefixes

| Prefix | Meaning | Example |
|---|---|---|
| a-, ab- | up, out; not; away | arise; abnormal; absent |
| anti- | against; prevents, cures | antiaircraft; antidote |
| contra- | opposed | contradict |
| de- | away from, off; down; reverse action of | derail; decline; defrost |
| dis- | lack of; not; away | distrust; dishonest; disarm |
| equi- | equal | equidistant |
| il-, im-, in-, ir- | not; in, into | illegal; investigate |
| inter- | between, among | international |
| mal- | bad | maltreat, malignant |
| mis- | wrong | misspell |
| non- | not | nonworking |
| post- | after in time or space | postpone |
| pre- | before | predawn |
| pro- | in favor of; forward, ahead | profamily; propel |
| re- | again; back | rethink; repay |
| semi- | half; twice in a period; partly | semicircle; semiannual; semiconscious |
| sub- | under, below | subzero |
| trans- | across; beyond | transcontinental; transcend |
| un- | not; reverse of | unhappy; unfasten |

Vocabulary in Context G7, SV 9780547625805

# Suffixes

## Noun Suffixes

| Suffix | Example | Suffix | Example |
|---|---|---|---|
| *-ance, -ancy, -ence* | vigilance, vacancy, independence | *-ism* | realism, federalism |
| *-ant* | commandant, occupant | *-ist* | geologist |
| *-ation, -ion, -ition* | imagination, inspection, recognition | *-ity, -ty* | sincerity, frailty |
| *-cy* | accuracy | *-ment* | encouragement, commitment |
| *-eer, -er* | auctioneer, manager | *-ness* | kindness, fondness |
| *-hood* | womanhood, brotherhood | *-or* | counselor |
| *-ice* | cowardice, prejudice | *-ship* | ownership, worship |
| *-ician* | beautician, statistician | *-tude* | gratitude, solitude |

## Adjective Suffixes

| Suffix | Meaning | Example |
|---|---|---|
| *-able, -ible* | able to be | readable, convertible |
| *-al, -ant, -ar* | relating to | musical, triumphant, polar |
| *-ate* | having, full of | passionate |
| *-ful* | full of | harmful |
| *-ic, -ish* | pertaining to, like | heroic, foolish |
| *-ive* | pertaining to | descriptive |
| *-less* | without | senseless |
| *-like, -ly* | like | lifelike, scholarly |
| *-most* | at the extreme | topmost |
| *-ous* | full of | furious |
| *-or* | one who | actor |
| *-y* | state of | funny |

## Verb Suffixes

| Suffix | Meaning | Example |
|---|---|---|
| *-ate, -fy* | to make | activate, simplify |
| *-en, -ise, -ize* | to become | strengthen, merchandise, computerize |

## Adverb Suffixes

| Suffix | Meaning | Example |
|---|---|---|
| *-ily, -ly* | manner | happily, quickly |
| *-ward* | toward | skyward |
| *-wise* | like | clockwise |

Vocabulary in Context G7, SV 9780547625805

## Roots and Word Families

A word root cannot stand alone but must be combined with other word parts. A great many roots used in our language come from Greek or Latin. A single root can generate many English words.

### Useful Greek Roots

| Root | Meaning | Example |
|------|---------|---------|
| *aster, astr* | star | asterisk |
| *auto* | self, alone | autobiography |
| *bibl, biblio* | book | bibliography |
| *bi, bio* | life | biology |
| *chron* | time | chronology |
| *cracy, crat* | rule, government | democracy |
| *gram, graph* | write, draw, describe | grammar, paragraph |
| *meter, metr* | measure | barometer |
| *neo* | new | neoclassical |
| *ortho* | straight, correct | orthodontist, orthodox |
| *phob* | fear | claustrophobia |
| *phon* | sound | phonograph |
| *psych* | mind, soul, spirit | psychology |
| *scope* | see | telescope |
| *tele* | far, distant | television |
| *therm* | heat | thermometer |

### Useful Latin Roots

| Root | Meaning | Example |
|------|---------|---------|
| *capt, cept* | take, have | capture, accept |
| *cede, ceed, cess* | go, yield, give way | secede, proceed, recess |
| *dic, dict* | speak, say, tell | dictate, dictionary |
| *duc, duct* | lead | introduce, conductor |
| *fact, fect* | do, make | factory, defect |
| *ject* | throw, hurl | eject, inject |
| *mob, mot, mov* | move | mobility, motion, movie |
| *pon, pos, posit* | place, put | opponent, deposit |
| *port* | carry | porter, portable |
| *puls* | throb, urge | pulsate, compulsory |
| *scrib, script* | write | prescribe, scripture |
| *tain, ten, tent* | hold | contain, tenant, attention |
| *ven, vent* | come | convention, event |
| *vers, vert* | turn | versatile, invert |
| *vid, vis* | see | video, vista |
| *voc, vok* | voice, call | vocal, invoke |

# Reading Clouds

by Howard Peet

Read the selection. Think about the meanings of the **boldfaced** words. Then go back to the selection. Underline the words or sentences that give you a clue to the meaning of each **boldfaced** word.

---

*Have you ever noticed the differences in clouds? Some look like fluffy cotton balls, while others look like wide white sheets. The following selection tells you what these differences mean.*

If you ranked the topics of conversation in people's lives, weather would probably end up at or near the top. Everyone from philosopher to **florist** feels free to comment on the weather and to guess what tomorrow's weather will be. However, the best guessers are people who **observe** the **development** of clouds, for clouds are the makers of weather.

In 1803, Luke Howard, an English **chemist**, was the first to **establish** names for different types of clouds. Howard believed that the shapes and forms of clouds were **inseparable** from the weather they caused. By naming the types of clouds, Howard began a scientific means of weather **prediction**.

Although there are many combinations of cloud forms, a good observer can **detect** four basic **formations**: cirrus, nimbus, stratus, and cumulus. The first three types signal that bad weather is either here or on the way.

Cirrus clouds **frequently** soar as high as ten miles. These clouds look like the remains of a pillow fight **conducted** so forcefully that feathers fly all over the room. Although there is no **guarantee**, cirrus clouds usually mean rainy or snowy **conditions** in ten to thirty hours.

When it is already raining or snowing, nimbus clouds are probably responsible. These are the dark rain clouds that often cannot be seen because of the rain or snow falling from them.

Sheetlike clouds that often blanket the ground are called stratus clouds. They can be a **handicap** to safe driving. Stratus clouds often appear as fog.

Vocabulary in Context G7, SV 9780547625805

The clouds that people enjoy the most are cumulus clouds. They are beautiful, and their presence usually means fair weather. Floating slowly along about one mile above the ground, these huge heaps of cotton **render magnificent**-looking scenes.

Identifying these four types of clouds can be **informative** as well as fun. Professional weather forecasters use information about clouds in a region to make their predictions. Accurate forecasting is very important; it can **safeguard** people from disastrous storms. However, the forecaster's job is difficult. For example, **seasonal** differences in weather patterns must be considered. Also, sudden changes in air pressure and wind speed can **alter** the weather greatly and unexpectedly. Weather forecasting may be a science, but it is not yet an exact one.

Vocabulary in Context G7, SV 9780547625805

# Context Clues

For each sentence, write the letter of the word or phrase that is closest in meaning to the word or words in italics. Use context clues to help you choose the correct answer.

Vocabulary in Context

_____ 1. Some scientists warn that if we continue to pollute the world, we could *alter* Earth's climates by raising temperatures significantly.

    **A** understand      **B** preserve      **C** improve      **D** change

_____ 2. Because Jim enjoys working in the science laboratory at school, his teacher has hopes that Jim will become *a chemist* someday.

    **A** a builder      **B** a teacher      **C** a weather forecaster      **D** an expert in chemistry

_____ 3. We left the room in good *condition*, with the carpet vacuumed and all the furniture dusted and set back in place.

    **A** control      **B** favor      **C** order      **D** design

_____ 4. Detective Hayes *conducted* the investigation of the robbery. He told each member of the team what to do and when to do it.

    **A** prevented      **B** managed      **C** followed      **D** aided

_____ 5. After a careful examination with her stethoscope, Dr. Maeda was able to *detect* a faint murmur in the patient's heart.

    **A** remove      **B** operate      **C** overlook      **D** discover

_____ 6. The young parents were fascinated by every stage of their baby's *development*, from his first smile to his first wobbly step.

    **A** growth      **B** education      **C** success      **D** personality

_____ 7. Congressman Romero will *establish* the social service program by organizing volunteers and building neighborhood shelters for the homeless.

    **A** close      **B** argue for      **C** set up      **D** overthrow

_____ 8. Dad sometimes brings Mom flowers from the *florist* near the train station.

    **A** flower seller      **B** tile layer      **C** restaurant      **D** engineer

_____ 9. Glaciers moving over North America created many of the *formations* of the hills and valleys that we see today.

    **A** arrangements      **B** future possibilities      **C** disappearances      **D** earthquakes

_____ 10. Because Renee spends all of her allowance on CDs, she is *frequently* in debt and looking for odd jobs to earn money.

    **A** rarely      **B** often      **C** occasionally      **D** never

_____ **11.** The company *guarantees* in writing that if its MP3 player has any defects, the device will be repaired or replaced free of charge.

    **A** demands      **B** admits      **C** promises      **D** denies

_____ **12.** Several months after injuring her back in an automobile accident, Becky finally began to accept her *handicap*.

    **A** insurance      **B** surgery      **C** confusion      **D** disability

_____ **13.** Officer McKenzie's lecture on neighborhood gangs was very *informative*. We learned some things we had not known.

    **A** educational      **B** casual      **C** boring      **D** businesslike

_____ **14.** Mario and Rosa are *inseparable*; they were together all summer and continue to spend time with each other as often as possible.

    **A** related      **B** close      **C** sensible      **D** boring

_____ **15.** The big Fourth of July fireworks display was *magnificent*. We'll always remember how beautiful it was.

    **A** dangerous      **B** loud      **C** splendid      **D** ordinary

_____ **16.** An astronomer *observes* the stars through a telescope, which makes it possible to see incredible distances.

    **A** watches      **B** connects      **C** arranges      **D** reveals

_____ **17.** The weather *prediction* was for hot weather—temperatures above one hundred for the next week.

    **A** invitation      **B** forecast      **C** contract      **D** prayer

_____ **18.** Our teacher *renders* a great service by offering help to students after school.

    **A** provides      **B** endures      **C** withholds      **D** repeats

_____ **19.** Wearing a life jacket serves as a *safeguard* against drowning.

    **A** relief      **B** protection      **C** pad      **D** hazard

_____ **20.** The work of migrant farmhands who follow the harvest is *seasonal*. Different crops are ready for harvest at different times of the year.

    **A** limited to water            **C** incredibly difficult

    **B** never ending            **D** dependent on the time of year

**Vocabulary in Context**

         Vocabulary in Context G7, SV 9780547625805

# Word Maze

All the words in the box are hidden in the maze. The words are arranged forward, backward, up, down, and diagonally. Put a circle around each word as you find it and cross the word off the list. Different words may overlap and use the same letter.

| | | | | |
|---|---|---|---|---|
| alter | chemist | condition | conduct | detect |
| development | establish | florist | formations | frequently |
| guarantee | handicap | informative | inseparable | magnificent |
| observe | prediction | render | safeguard | seasonal |

```
U  N  Y  L  T  N  E  U  Q  E  R  F  L  E  O
A  S  W  E  S  T  A  B  L  I  S  H  L  L  M
H  A  N  D  I  C  A  P  T  F  C  B  I  B  H
U  F  V  E  R  E  T  L  A  O  A  D  N  E  Q
R  E  R  T  O  F  H  I  G  R  N  E  F  V  N
E  G  R  E  L  J  Q  U  A  M  O  V  O  R  O
N  U  E  C  F  C  A  P  C  A  I  E  R  E  I
D  A  D  T  L  R  E  B  O  T  T  L  M  S  T
E  R  I  P  A  S  M  R  N  I  I  O  A  B  C
R  D  B  N  N  V  K  W  D  O  D  P  T  O  I
D  K  T  I  Y  B  F  W  U  N  N  M  I  R  D
S  E  A  S  O  N  A  L  C  S  O  E  V  P  E
E  L  C  H  E  M  I  S  T  Y  C  N  E  G  R
C  M  A  G  N  I  F  I  C  E  N  T  E  B  P
```

Vocabulary in Context G7, SV 9780547625805

Vocabulary in Context

# Standardized Test Practice

Circle the letter of the word that is closest in meaning to the capitalized word.

**TIP** Always read all the answer choices. Many choices may make sense. But only one answer choice has a meaning similar to that of the capitalized word.

1. DETECT

   **A** destroy          **B** confuse          **C** discover          **D** arrest

2. ESTABLISH

   **A** create           **B** change           **C** return            **D** protect

3. FREQUENTLY

   **A** often            **B** occasionally      **C** seldom            **D** honestly

4. GUARANTEE

   **A** forecast         **B** quality           **C** advertisement     **D** promise

5. HANDICAP

   **A** discussion       **B** ability           **C** disadvantage      **D** error

6. INFORMATIVE

   **A** imaginative      **B** useless           **C** entertaining      **D** instructive

7. MAGNIFICENT

   **A** distant          **B** expensive         **C** glorious          **D** smart

8. OBSERVE

   **A** neglect          **B** miss              **C** view              **D** understand

9. ALTER

   **A** separate         **B** change            **C** forecast          **D** create

10. SAFEGUARD

   **A** hazard           **B** fort              **C** cruise            **D** defend

**13**

# Understanding Related Words

The words in the box are closely related to the vocabulary words. See how many of the words you already know. Use the glossary to find the definitions of unfamiliar words.

| | | | | |
|---|---|---|---|---|
| alterations | conductor | detector | develop | floral |
| frequency | handicapped | magnify | observation | reestablish |

Write the word from the box that best completes the meaning of the sentence.

1. The _____ delivered the _____ arrangement just before the party. (floral, florist)

2. We _____ have difficulty finding the correct _____ of that radio station. (frequency, frequently)

3. Tony _____ a tour through the opera house, during which visitors were able

    to meet the _____ of the orchestra. (conducted, conductor)

4. Although Tamika is _____, she does not allow her limitations to

    _____ her daily life. (handicap, handicapped)

5. Though it was cloudy, we tried to _____ the city from the

    _____ deck on the twenty-fifth floor. (observation, observe)

6. The seamstress is good at making _____, so I'm going to ask her to

    _____ my new pants since they're too long. (alter, alterations)

7. My uncle uses a metal _____ to try to _____ buried metal objects in the sand at the beach. (detect, detector)

8. The builder has drawn up plans for a new housing _____, and he

    wants to _____ two other neighborhoods over the next two years.
    (develop, development)

9. After using the binoculars to _____ my view of the hawks, I had a

    _____ look at the rare birds. (magnify, magnificent)

10. First you need to _____ the Internet connection you previously lost, and

    then you can _____ successful e-mail communication with your friends.
    (establish, reestablish)

**Word Skills**

# Sentence Completion

Write the word from the box that best completes the meaning of the sentence.

| chemist | conductor | develop | flora | infrequently |
|---------|-----------|---------|-------|--------------|
| separate | magnificent | observation | rendered | season |

1. The genius behind the famous cosmetic product is the _____ in the laboratory.

2. The _____ in the Amazon rainforest is abundant due to its wet season.

3. From the _____ tower, the firefighters can see for miles.

4. Please _____ the map pencils into groups by color.

5. After the orchestra's performance, the _____ and the musicians took a bow.

6. In order to make his sisters laugh, Luis _____ an amusing imitation of an angry dog.

7. The red sun setting above the blue water of the Gulf of Mexico was a

_____ sight.

8. Because Sasha has a library available to her, she _____ buys books from a bookstore.

9. LeeAnn will have to wait for a warmer _____ to wear her lightweight jacket.

10. The doctors and scientists report that they will _____ a new study in cancer treatment.

**Word Skills**

# The Prefix *un-*

The prefix *un-* means "not." For example, the word *unsatisfied* means "not satisfied." *Un-* can also mean the reverse of some situation or condition, as in the word *unfasten*. Match each word on the left with its definition on the right. Write the letter of the definition on the line.

_____ 1. undetected      **A.** not set up; unsettled

_____ 2. unestablished      **B.** unusual for a certain time of year

_____ 3. unobserved      **C.** not watched

_____ 4. unaltered      **D.** not discovered

_____ 5. unseasonable      **E.** not changed

# The Suffix *-ion*

The suffix *-ion*, when added to a verb, means "the act or state of." If the word *predict* means "to foretell the future," the word *prediction* means "the act of foretelling the future." Match each word on the left with its definition on the right. Write the letter of the definition on the line.

_____ 1. conduction      **A.** the act of observing or watching

_____ 2. alteration      **B.** the process of making something look larger

_____ 3. observation      **C.** the act of transferring or transmitting

_____ 4. magnification      **D.** the act of discovering

_____ 5. detection      **E.** the act of changing something

# The Latin Root *magni*

The word *magnificent* comes from the Latin word *magnus*, meaning "great." The two related words *magnificence* and *magnify* also come from this Latin word. Look up the meanings of these two words. Then complete each of the following sentences with one of the two words.

1. A telescope serves to _____ the stars.

2. Visitors to Washington, D.C., are impressed by the _____ of the Lincoln Memorial.

3. The dark blue dress served to _____ Susan's blue eyes.

4. Joni's refusal to make friends only served to _____ her loneliness.

5. Stained glass windows in a cathedral add to its _____.

     Vocabulary in Context G7, SV 9780547625805

Name _____  Date _____

# Writing

Many products are sold with a guarantee—a declaration that for a certain number of months after a sale, the product will be fixed free of charge to the owner. (This is often referred to as a warranty.)

What would be the ideal written guarantee for a CD player or an MP3 player? What parts and what service would be included? What exclusions, if any, would be mentioned? Where would the product be serviced? Who would be responsible for the mailing costs? On the lines below, write a guarantee for a product. Use some vocabulary words from this unit in your writing.

_____

_____

_____

_____

_____

_____

_____

_____

_____

_____

_____

_____

_____

Writing

# The Press and Free Speech

by Howard Peet

Read the selection. Think about the meanings of the **boldfaced** words. Then go back to the selection. Underline the words or sentences that give you a clue to the meaning of each **boldfaced** word.

---

*The following reading selection explains why reporting a news story is often difficult and sometimes dangerous.*

**Inviting** as it may sound, the job of a **journalist** is not an easy one. In any one day on the job, a reporter may be **doused** with rain or threatened with a lawsuit. Whatever happens, the most important task is to give an honest account of **actual** events. When two reporters write different **versions** of the same story, one version might be more colorful than the other. However, accuracy is what counts most. In giving the news, it is better to be **reliable** than **vivid**. A good reporter will try for both.

Reporters, like the rest of us, live in an **impure** world, so the **pursuit** of the news sometimes involves mystery and **intrigue**. Especially in **metropolitan** areas, people with inside information about crime may be afraid to talk about it. They may not want to be seen **lingering** at the scene of a crime, talking to reporters. Sometimes a person with inside information only can be **maneuvered** into giving information by being promised complete privacy. The reporter must promise not to reveal the person's name.

Freedom of the press is guaranteed by the First Amendment to the U.S. Constitution. Journalists—and most courts—have interpreted freedom of the press as meaning that journalists need not reveal their sources for a story. The public is often **unaware** of the **hazardous** situation journalists could face if this were not true. Journalists are caught between wanting to **acknowledge** their sources and needing to protect them. Judges and attorneys sometimes claim that members of the media **hinder** justice by failing to **disclose** the insider's name. The journalist, however, may insist that the only way the insider will give information is if he or she remains nameless. In extreme circumstances, the informant's life may be in danger if his or her name is made public.

Knowing this, journalists may face a **solemn** decision. They know that they cannot be **unaccountable** for their actions. They may decide to go to jail rather than reveal the names of informants who trusted them. Over the years a number of journalists have, in fact, been jailed for this reason. However, all of the journalists who have refused to reveal the names of their informants have eventually been released.

# Context Clues

For each sentence, write the letter of the word or phrase that is closest in meaning to the word or words in italics. Use context clues to help you choose the correct answer.

_____ 1. The shoplifter *acknowledged* his guilt and apologized for stealing the tool.

    **A** admitted     **B** forgot     **C** argued     **D** denied

_____ 2. The *actual* cost of the car rental could be found by adding on the price of insurance and mileage, plus tax.

    **A** efficient     **B** reduced     **C** imaginary     **D** real

_____ 3. At the press conference the President freely *disclosed* the terms and details of the peace treaty.

    **A** concealed     **B** suspended     **C** resisted     **D** made known

_____ 4. When the swim team won, the team members *doused* their coach with lemonade from a huge container.

    **A** teased     **B** soaked     **C** watched     **D** insulted

_____ 5. The drifting snow made driving *hazardous* and forced many people off the road.

    **A** suitable     **B** dangerous     **C** possible     **D** vital

_____ 6. Lack of money for costumes and stage sets *hindered* the young theater company and delayed its opening date.

    **A** encouraged     **B** held back     **C** developed     **D** streamlined

_____ 7. Although the water looked *impure* and unhealthy, tests proved it to be safe.

    **A** inviting     **B** polluted     **C** tranquil     **D** vital

_____ 8. Mystery stories *intrigue* many readers; these readers eagerly await the next tale by their favorite author.

    **A** greatly interest     **B** bore     **C** discourage     **D** challenge

_____ 9. On a hot summer day, a cold, clear lake looks very *inviting*.

    **A** appealing     **B** distant     **C** technical     **D** threatening

Vocabulary in Context

_____ **10.** After a verdict was reached, the *journalists* rushed from the courtroom to call their editors and write their stories.

    **A** technicians     **B** judges     **C** witnesses     **D** news reporters

_____ **11.** We *lingered* over dinner, neither of us willing to make the first move toward ending the meal.

    **A** hurried     **B** met     **C** skipped     **D** took extra time

_____ **12.** The skilled driver carefully *maneuvered* the boat onto the trailer.

    **A** floated     **B** moved     **C** slowed     **D** lived

_____ **13.** The weather forecast was only for the *metropolitan* area, not the outlying farm communities.

    **A** rural     **B** distant     **C** urban     **D** inhabited

_____ **14.** In *pursuit of* world conquest, Alexander the Great led his armies across Asia.

    **A** avoiding     **B** resisting     **C** suspending     **D** seeking

_____ **15.** That encyclopedia is a *reliable* source of information; each fact has been carefully checked.

    **A** favorite     **B** personal     **C** dependable     **D** neglected

_____ **16.** The nation was in a *solemn* mood for some time after President John F. Kennedy was assassinated in 1963.

    **A** serious     **B** suspenseful     **C** peaceful     **D** angry

_____ **17.** James was considered to be *unaccountable* for the loss of the necklace because it had disappeared before his employment began.

    **A** a suspect for     **B** guilty of     **C** not responsible for     **D** unhappy about

_____ **18.** The deer calmly munched the grass, *unaware* of the mountain lion's presence.

    **A** suspicious     **B** not knowing     **C** glad     **D** conscious

_____ **19.** Hugo and Eduardo had different *versions* of the accident. Hugo claimed the driver was at fault; Eduardo said the driver was innocent.

    **A** reactions to     **B** fears about     **C** dreams of     **D** descriptions of

_____ **20.** The interior decorator recommended *vivid* colors to brighten the drab room.

    **A** bright     **B** soft     **C** pale     **D** plain

# Word Maze

All the words in the list below are hidden in the maze. The words are arranged forward, backward, up, down, and diagonally. Put a circle around each word as you find it and cross the word off the list. Different words may overlap and use the same letter.

| acknowledge | lingering | actual | maneuver | disclose |
|---|---|---|---|---|
| metropolitan | doused | pursuit | hazardous | solemn |
| hinder | unaccountable | impure | unaware | intrigue |
| versions | inviting | vivid | journalist | reliable |

```
I  P  J  M  E  T  R  O  P  O  L  I  T  A  N  J  T  T
C  D  W  O  D  N  E  A  C  E  R  S  E  E  Z  O  O  U
Q  M  F  X  U  R  R  G  H  L  O  L  Z  U  S  U  S  S
K  N  U  C  U  R  W  I  T  B  B  L  A  G  N  R  P  N
L  O  K  P  S  V  N  M  R  A  Q  P  D  I  O  N  A  U
A  V  M  U  I  D  F  A  T  I  X  U  O  R  I  A  R  P
U  I  Y  V  E  Z  C  N  L  L  O  G  U  T  S  L  Y  M
T  U  I  R  N  G  U  O  F  E  Z  G  S  N  R  I  G  A
C  D  H  Z  Z  O  D  K  U  R  S  Z  E  I  E  S  E  N
A  B  G  A  C  H  H  E  E  I  J  T  D  K  V  T  A  E
P  K  P  C  V  L  B  R  I  N  V  I  T  I  N  G  J  U
V  A  A  G  X  E  G  D  E  L  W  O  N  K  C  A  G  V
S  N  Q  U  N  A  W  A  R  E  D  A  C  X  B  N  A  E
U  F  I  O  Z  G  G  E  L  I  N  G  E  R  I  N  G  R
Z  H  A  Z  A  R  D  O  U  S  L  L  K  H  M  B  O  O
T  I  U  S  R  U  P  T  G  M  P  H  S  O  L  E  M  N
W  B  F  E  D  D  I  S  C  L  O  S  E  D  G  M  O  X
J  M  C  S  B  P  E  Q  C  K  W  E  W  L  M  I  B  M
```

Vocabulary in Context G7, SV 9780547625805

# Standardized Test Practice

Circle the letter of the word that is most nearly *opposite* in meaning to the capitalized word.

**TIP**

Always read all the answer choices. Many choices may make sense. But only one answer choice has the *opposite* meaning as the capitalized word.

1. ACKNOWLEDGE
   A know         B deny         C recognize         D agree

2. ACTUAL
   A dishonest    B imaginary    C realistic         D unusual

3. DISCLOSE
   A hide         B emphasize    C display           D decide

4. HAZARDOUS
   A brave        B dangerous    C safe              D cowardly

5. HINDER
   A obstruct     B establish    C assist            D follow

6. LINGER
   A decide       B merge        C spread            D hurry

7. METROPOLITAN
   A crowded      B awkward      C rural             D urban

8. RELIABLE
   A undependable B true         C determined        D strange

9. SOLEMN
   A heavy        B false        C repulsive         D humorous

10. VIVID
    A memorable   B polite       C natural           D dull

# Finding Examples

The words in the box are closely related to the vocabulary words. See how many of the words you already know. Use the glossary to find the definitions of unfamiliar words.

| | | | | |
|---|---|---|---|---|
| hazard | hindrance | reliance | impurity | awareness |
| invitation | reliability | disclosure | solemnity | intriguing |

Write the letter of the situation that best demonstrates the meaning of the boldfaced word.

_____ **1. hazard**

   **A** Maria left her roller skates at the bottom of the stairs.

   **B** The highway department installed traffic signals at the busy intersection.

   **C** No matter how late he goes to bed, Kyle always gets up early.

_____ **2. hindrance**

   **A** The company sponsors an annual race.

   **B** Lack of experience can make it difficult to get a job.

   **C** Your work has shown steady improvement.

_____ **3. reliance**

   **A** In the attic, we found trunks filled with scrapbooks.

   **B** The Armstrongs know they can count on their friends to help with the move.

   **C** Susan often trusts the wrong people.

_____ **4. impurity**

   **A** The baker's specialty is four-grain bread.

   **B** The jeweler examined the diamond for flaws.

   **C** A witness testifies without fear of punishment.

_____ **5. awareness**

   **A** Northern China has a cold, dry climate.

   **B** Lydia doesn't enjoy camping in the winter.

   **C** When a car pulls into the driveway, the dog begins barking.

_____ **6. invitation**

   **A** The police officer directed motorists around the accident.

   **B** Tina asked ten friends to attend her birthday party.

   **C** The bill arrived in today's mail.

**Word Skills**

_____ **7. reliability**

    **A** The most brilliant student does not always earn the highest grades.

    **B** Keiko has never failed to turn in his assignments on time.

    **C** The Chinese invented gunpowder.

_____ **8. disclosure**

    **A** The veterans will march at the head of the parade.

    **B** Chief Tanaka explained what the department knew about the case.

    **C** The city erected a fence around the swimming pool.

_____ **9. solemnity**

    **A** A reception, including a dance party, followed the wedding.

    **B** The funeral procession moved slowly down the street.

    **C** The hail destroyed the corn crop.

_____ **10. intriguing**

    **A** Germany's invasion of Poland was the beginning of World War II.

    **B** Steel is a mixture of iron and other minerals.

    **C** Noah finds anything related to computers fascinating.

**Word Skills**

Vocabulary in Context G7, SV 9780547625805

Name _____ Date _____

# Finding the Unrelated Word

Write the letter of the word that is not related in meaning to the other words in the set.

_____ 1. **A** soak     **B** douse     **C** grasp     **D** drench

_____ 2. **A** impure     **B** clean     **C** dirty     **D** polluted

_____ 3. **A** scheme     **B** intrigue     **C** plot     **D** stamina

_____ 4. **A** solid     **B** faithful     **C** reliable     **D** magnificent

_____ 5. **A** acknowledge     **B** admit     **C** predict     **D** confess

_____ 6. **A** proceed     **B** linger     **C** pause     **D** delay

_____ 7. **A** disclose     **B** show     **C** reveal     **D** hide

_____ 8. **A** hunt     **B** chase     **C** cluster     **D** pursuit

_____ 9. **A** blameable     **B** unaccountable     **C** guilty     **D** responsible

_____ 10. **A** report     **B** version     **C** writer     **D** description

# Compare and Contrast

Complete the following sentences to describe how the two things named are alike or different.

1. *Speaking vividly* is like *talking* except that _____

_____.

2. Being *aware* is like being *mindful* because _____

_____.

3. A *journal* is like a *diary* because _____

_____.

4. *Peacefulness* is like *solemnness* except that _____

_____.

5. A *hazard* is like a *chance* except that _____

_____.

# The Prefixes *im-* and *un-*

The prefixes *im-* and *un-* generally mean "not." The words *impure*, *unaccountable*, and *unaware* are examples of words that use these prefixes. Other prefixes that often mean not are *in-*, *il-*, *ir-*, and *non-*.

Add either *im-* or *un-* to the words below. Write the newly formed word and then write the meaning of the new word, using a dictionary to check your work.

1. **reliable**

   New word: _____

   Definition: _____

   _____

2. **inviting**

   New word: _____

   Definition: _____

   _____

3. **mature**

   New word: _____

   Definition: _____

   _____

4. **suitable**

   New word: _____

   Definition: _____

   _____

5. **movable**

   New word: _____

   Definition: _____

   _____

**Word Skills**

# Writing

Choose one item from each of the three columns below. Using your imagination and some of the vocabulary words from this unit, write a story based on your three items.

| Characters | Incidents | Conditions |
| --- | --- | --- |

**Characters**

- an eager journalist
- a reliable friend
- a person unaware of danger
- a person accountable for his or her actions
- a solemn judge

**Incidents**

- lingering without reason
- maneuvering around obstacles
- acknowledging the truth
- disclosing the secret
- intrigued by the mystery

**Conditions**

- in an inviting way
- with a vivid imagination
- in hot pursuit of the criminal
- in a metropolitan area
- in a hazardous situation

_____

_____

_____

_____

_____

_____

_____

_____

_____

_____

_____

_____

Writing

Vocabulary in Context G7, SV 9780547625805

# The Final Entry

by Howard Peet

Read the story below. Think about the meanings of the **boldfaced** words. Then go back to the story. Underline the words or sentences that give you a clue to the meaning of each **boldfaced** word.

---

*What unforeseen problems await future space travelers? In the following science fiction story, a space crew encounters a startling change.*

The *Star Shot* burst into outer space like a meteor. Heading for the Virgo **cluster** of galaxies light years away was a **venture** of faith and courage. The crew approached the **mission** with great **zeal** and confidence. Their spaceship, after all, was a **testimony** to the latest scientific advances. The tremendous speed of the *Star Shot* allowed the crew to go deeper into space than anyone had gone before.

Each crew member, from **technician** to commander, had been carefully chosen. Even the mascot, a chimpanzee named Jocko, was the result of a lengthy **quest**. Jocko was intelligent and **curious**, even for a chimpanzee, and his crazy antics **endeared** him to the crew.

The journey was as smooth as silk until the spaceship left Earth's solar system. Then a strange thing began to happen. The farther the *Star Shot* traveled, the more knowledge each crew member's brain **accumulated**. As the crew members' brains accumulated more knowledge, their heads began to grow. Soon their heads were **abnormal** sizes. Worse yet, their heads kept growing. The situation quickly passed from **desperate** to hopeless. Back on Earth there was no contact with the *Star Shot*; the ship never returned.

Many years later, the *Star Shot* was found floating aimlessly through the Virgo galaxies. Commander Flynn of the spaceship *Advance* ordered an examining party to board the *Star Shot*. **Suspense** aboard the *Advance* grew as the rescue crew awaited word from the examining party. Had the *Star Shot* fallen victim to a **mutiny** or some strange sickness?

The leader of the examining party, Captain Lewis, returned with the leader of the *Star Shot's* logbook gripped tightly in his hand. Terror enveloped him in a radiating force. Standing **mute**, he pointed to the final entry in the log. It read:

November 11, 2101

They are all dead but me. Their huge heads are as large as their bodies. Their staring eyes are so **repulsive** that I must look away as I write these last words. What little **effectiveness** I still have is being poured into this message. I feel death's cold fingers gripping my heart. I only hope that whoever finds this will be able to read my handwriting. My despair is a shadow on my soul.

As my **untimely** death draws near, I leave this final message. It is **vital** that future galaxy travelers heed this warning:

BEWARE OF THE **TRANSFORMATION** THAT COMES
FROM ACCUMULATING KNOWLEDGE TOO QUICKLY.

Farewell,
Jocko

Name _____  Date _____

# Understanding Figurative Language

Writers often use **figurative language**, or figures of speech, to help their readers visualize or imagine the images they are describing. Below are three types of figurative language that appear in the story "The Final Entry." Read about these figures of speech. Then answer the questions that follow.

---

**Simile:** A simile is a figure of speech that compares two things using the words *like* or *as*.

Examples:     The ice was as smooth as glass.

                 The rabbit's fur felt like cotton balls when I petted him.

**Metaphor:** A metaphor is a figure of speech that compares two things by stating that one thing *is* something else.

Examples:     The baby's smile was a beam of sunlight to the mother's eyes.

                 Spring is a rainbow of beauty and joy.

**Personification:** Personification is a figure of speech in which an object is given human attributes or characteristics.

Examples:     The tree hugged us with its warm, shadowy embrace.

                 The clouds raced eagerly across the sunny sky.

---

1. Which of the sentences from the story contains an example of a **simile**?

   **A** The *Star Shot* burst into outer space like a meteor.

   **B** Heading for the Virgo cluster of galaxies light years away was a venture of faith and courage.

   **C** The crew approached the mission with great zeal and confidence.

   **D** Their spaceship, after all, was a testimony to the latest scientific advances.

2. Which of the sentences from the story contains an example of **personification**?

   **A** They are all dead but me.

   **B** Their huge heads are as large as their bodies.

   **C** What little effectiveness I still have is being poured into this message.

   **D** I feel death's cold fingers gripping my heart.

3. Which of the sentences from the story contains an example of a **metaphor**?

   **A** I only hope that whoever finds this will be able to read my handwriting.

   **B** My despair is a shadow on my soul.

   **C** As my untimely death draws near, I leave this final message.

   **D** It is vital that future galaxy travelers heed this warning.

Vocabulary in Context G7, SV 9780547625805

# Context Clues

For each sentence, write the letter of the word or phrase that is closest in meaning to the word or words in italics. Use context clues to help you choose the correct answer.

_____ 1. Eight feet is an *abnormal* height for a person. Only a few people have ever grown that tall.

    A impossible      B average      C unusual      D ordinary

_____ 2. Over a period of twenty years, Mr. Jiminez *accumulated* a fortune through hard work and wise saving.

    A spent      B collected      C lost      D altered

_____ 3. The grocery store serves a *cluster* of small towns in the rural area.

    A group      B separate      C large      D individual

_____ 4. Small children are *curious*; they ask many questions about things they see and hear.

    A fussy      B afraid of change      C restless      D eager to learn

_____ 5. Hanging by one arm from the cliff, Ricardo knew he was in *a desperate* situation.

    A a dangerous      B a tremendous      C a ridiculous      D an uncomfortable

_____ 6. The *effectiveness* of the cleanup campaign was evident as we drove through the spotless neighborhood.

    A success      B length      C failure      D difficulty

_____ 7. The courage with which Paulo faced his new handicap *endeared* him to us all. Everyone who knew Paulo liked him.

    A made him dependent on      C made him beloved by

    B made him different from      D made him bitter toward

_____ 8. Dr. Jonas Salk's *mission* was to rid the world of polio. In 1955, he succeeded in developing a vaccine that prevented the dreaded disease.

    A mistake      B special task      C religion      D careful observation

_____ 9. As Officer Tomito scolded him, Danny was *mute*, unable to speak.

    A deaf      B amazed      C speechless      D relieved

_____ 10. Because of the terrible conditions aboard the ship, the crew planned a *mutiny*.

    A party      B cleanup      C rebellion      D journey

**Vocabulary in Context**

Vocabulary in Context

**11.** In his *quest for* fame and fortune, Matthew traveled to the big city to try out for the major league team.

    **A** search for       **B** avoidance of       **C** guarantee of       **D** disappointment with

**12.** The refrigerator door was left open for days, and the smell of rotten food was *repulsive*.

    **A** harmful       **B** overflowing       **C** disgusting       **D** magnificent

**13.** The mystery story kept me in *suspense* until the final chapter, when I found out who the murderer was.

    **A** fear       **B** uncertainty       **C** laughter       **D** boredom

**14.** The critics praised the pianist for being a *technician* who performed the music without a flaw.

    **A** teacher       **B** skilled person       **C** volunteer       **D** manufacturer

**15.** The students and teachers presented their principal with a gold watch as *a testimony* of their respect and affection.

    **A** a trace       **B** an indication       **C** a denial       **D** an observation

**16.** The *transformation* of a caterpillar into a butterfly is a wonder of nature.

    **A** recognition       **B** changing       **C** collision       **D** removal

**17.** Nick's big mistake was his *untimely* interruption during our manager's speech.

    **A** thoughtful       **B** creative       **C** appropriate       **D** inappropriate

**18.** Mr. Lyon's *venture into* the restaurant business proved very successful. He began with one restaurant and expanded to ten.

    **A** remark about       **B** entry into       **C** visit to       **D** departure from

**19.** The environment is one of the most *vital* concerns of U.S. citizens.

    **A** important       **B** harmless       **C** dishonest       **D** unnecessary

**20.** The students had such *zeal for* the project that they enthusiastically devoted their weekend to finishing it.

    **A** dislike for       **B** eager interest in       **C** simple regard for       **D** mixed feelings about

Name _____ Date _____

# Crossword Puzzle

Use the words in the box and the clues to complete the crossword puzzle.

| abnormal | accumulated | cluster | curious | desperate | zeal |
|----------|-------------|---------|---------|-----------|------|
| effectiveness | endeared | mute | mission | mutiny | repulsive |
| suspense | technician | testimony | quest | vital | venture |

**Across**

2. Made beloved
4. A revolt against authority
5. Disgusting; upsetting
6. Unable to speak
7. One having special scientific or mechanical skills
10. Unusual or unnatural
11. Eager for information
13. A risky undertaking
14. Any form of evidence; a statement made by a witness under oath
16. Usefulness; forcefulness

**Down**

1. A search or journey
3. Extremely dangerous or serious; hopeless
4. The special duty that a person or group is sent to do
8. A group of people or things gathered together
9. Collected; piled up
12. Mental uncertainty; state of excitement regarding the outcome of an event
13. Essential or necessary
15. Enthusiasm

Name _____  Date _____

# Standardized Test Practice

Circle the letter of the word that is most nearly opposite in meaning to the capitalized word.

 **TIP**

> Always read all the answer choices. Many choices may make sense. Only one answer choice has the opposite meaning as the capitalized word.

**1.** CURIOUS

   **A** searching     **B** clever     **C** changeable     **D** uninterested

**2.** EFFECTIVENESS

   **A** foolishness     **B** stupidity     **C** uselessness     **D** usefulness

**3.** UNTIMELY

   **A** early     **B** fast     **C** well-timed     **D** famous

**4.** CLUSTER

   **A** arrangement     **B** team     **C** setting     **D** individual

**5.** SUSPENSE

   **A** comedy     **B** fiction     **C** certainty     **D** bravery

**6.** DESPERATE

   **A** generous     **B** usual     **C** calm     **D** hopeless

**7.** ABNORMAL

   **A** natural     **B** unusual     **C** incomplete     **D** meaningful

**8.** REPULSIVE

   **A** appealing     **B** boring     **C** disgusting     **D** smooth

**9.** ZEAL

   **A** eagerness     **B** sadness     **C** curiosity     **D** disinterest

**10.** VITAL

   **A** lively     **B** unnecessary     **C** guaranteed     **D** unknown

# Finding Examples

The words in the box are closely related to the vocabulary words. See how many of the words you already know. Use the glossary to find the definitions of unfamiliar words.

| | | | | |
|---|---|---|---|---|
| abnormality | accumulation | curiosity | desperation | effective |
| ineffective | suspend | suspenseful | technical | vitality |

Write the letter of the situation that best shows the meaning of the boldfaced word.

_____ **1. effective**

    **A** a medicine that did not cure your hay fever

    **B** a cleanser that removes stubborn stains from the bathroom tile

    **C** a drink that leaves you thirsty

_____ **2. vitality**

    **A** baking a fancy cake

    **B** sleeping late

    **C** running a ten-mile race

_____ **3. technical**

    **A** a school that provides computer-repair training courses

    **B** a bright, intense color used in motion pictures

    **C** running into an old friend at the mall

_____ **4. suspenseful**

    **A** an exciting movie with a scary ending

    **B** a basketball game with a fifty-point margin of victory

    **C** a geography lesson

_____ **5. curiosity**

    **A** an argument between a brother and a sister

    **B** a little boy taking apart an alarm clock

    **C** a music student practicing a lesson

_____ **6. desperation**

    **A** jumping out of a burning building

    **B** a person who gossips

    **C** a coach talking to team members

_____ **7. accumulation**

    **A** winning a race

    **B** dishes piled in a sink

    **C** refusing to work

**Word Skills**

# True-False

Decide whether each statement is true or false. Write *T* for True and *F* for False.

_____ **1.** Exercising twenty minutes every day is an act of *desperation*.

_____ **2.** Watching TV while reading is an *effective* way to study for a test.

_____ **3.** The athlete who won the competition has great *vitality*.

_____ **4.** His *curiosity* about dreams caused him to research the topic.

_____ **5.** Because the directions are *technical*, we can put the model together however we please.

_____ **6.** An *accumulation* of wealth means to lose it gradually over time.

_____ **7.** The movie was *suspenseful* because I had read the book.

_____ **8.** We must *suspend* the kite-flying contest because it's windy.

_____ **9.** A horse with four legs is an example of an *abnormality*.

_____ **10.** Her communication was *ineffective* because she never answered our questions.

# Finding the Unrelated Word

Write the letter of the word that is not related in meaning to the other words in the set.

_____ **1. A** mute     **B** silent     **C** speechless     **D** curious

_____ **2. A** effective     **B** competent     **C** weak     **D** useful

_____ **3. A** defeat     **B** quest     **C** adventure     **D** mission

_____ **4. A** abnormal     **B** different     **C** irregular     **D** effective

_____ **5. A** gather     **B** collect     **C** annoy     **D** accumulate

_____ **6. A** necessary     **B** essential     **C** untimely     **D** vital

**Word Skills**

# Writing

The vocabulary words from this unit include several adjectives: *abnormal*, *curious*, *desperate*, *mutiny*, *repulsive*, *untimely*, and *vital*. Write a short paragraph in which you use some of these adjectives to describe a person, a place, or an event from your own experience.

_____

_____

_____

_____

_____

_____

_____

_____

_____

_____

_____

_____

_____

Writing

# A Winner

### by Howard Peet

Read the selection. Think about the meanings of the **boldfaced** words. Then go back to the selection. Underline the words or sentences that give you a clue to the meaning of each **boldfaced** word.

---

*Each of us should aspire to do and be the best we can. Congresswoman Barbara Jordan is an excellent example of someone who did just that.*

Barbara Jordan's winning **attitude** brought her success in her many **endeavors**. President Lyndon B. Johnson once said of Jordan, "She proved that black is beautiful before we knew what it meant." He described her as "the epitome (model) of the new **politics**." Over the years Jordan's **dedication** to **social reform** gained her the **respect** of not only government officials but also that of the public.

The fact that Jordan was born in Houston, Texas, on February 21, 1936, to a poor, loving family helps explain her **legitimate concern** for social reform. However, it took **discipline** for Jordan to put her concern into action, a self-discipline learned from her father. He **ignited** her desire to seek out the best in herself. Jordan said that her father, a Baptist minister, had three great loves—his family, his faith, and his language. It was from him that she learned the **cultured** way of speaking that became her trademark.

Jordan's drive to achieve began to take shape early in her life. Hearing Edith Sampson, an African-American attorney, speak at Jordan's high school Career Day helped Jordan decide to become a lawyer. She graduated in 1956 from Texas Southern University, an all-black institution of higher learning. Pursuing her dream of becoming a lawyer, Jordan earned her law degree at Boston University in 1959.

Eventually Jordan turned her attention toward government service. She showed **determination**—and competitive spirit—by running for a seat in the Texas House of Representatives in 1962. She lost. She lost again in 1964. But Jordan **persevered**, and in 1966 she finally won a seat in the Texas Senate.

In the state senate, Jordan **upheld** her belief in the need for social reform. She saw to it that laws were passed to help "the really poor people—laundry workers, domestic [and] farm workers." She also used her influence to see that these laws were **enforced**. As a result of her efforts, she was named the outstanding new senator during her first year in office.

After several years in state government, Jordan directed her efforts toward the federal government. In 1972, it was Jordan **versus** Merritt for the United States Congress. Jordan won by more than 85,000 votes.

Until her retirement from Congress at the end of 1978, her **policy** remained a simple one. She stated what she felt to be her **civic obligation** by saying, "I am here simply because all those people in the 18th District of Texas cannot get on planes and buses and come to Washington to speak for themselves. They have elected me as their spokesperson, nothing else, and my only job is to speak for them. That is the job of every one of the people's representatives."

Barbara Jordan was respected by Republicans and Democrats alike. However, what probably made her a winner was that she respected herself. Following a glowing introduction from President Johnson's widow at the National Women's Conference in Houston in 1977, Jordan said, "Thank you, all of you, and thank you, Lady Bird Johnson, for an introduction of which I am worthy."

Upon her death in 1996, Jordan lay in state on the campus of the University of Texas at Austin. She was the first black woman to be buried in the Texas State Cemetery in Austin.

BARBARA JORDAN

# Context Clues

For each sentence, write the letter of the word or phrase that is closest in meaning to the word or words in italics. Use context clues to help you choose the correct answer.

_____ 1. Lee's success in school is due in part to his positive *attitude*. He approaches each task with the belief that he will do well.

    **A** grades      **B** way of thinking      **C** teacher      **D** schedule

_____ 2. *Civic* responsibilities keep Senator Barrientos busy day and night. As an elected official, she is always trying to solve problems that affect the citizens of her state.

    **A** technical      **B** family      **C** community      **D** scientific

_____ 3. Because he loves animals, Julio has a *concern* for the decent treatment of stray dogs and cats.

    **A** lack of feeling for          **C** complete inattention to
    **B** disagreement with         **D** strong interest in

_____ 4. Unlike Mr. Chase, who had a rude, rough way of putting things, Ms. Upton spoke in a sophisticated, *cultured* way that impressed us.

    **A** crude      **B** educated      **C** obvious      **D** abrupt

_____ 5. Jake regularly volunteers at the shelter, and he frequently writes letters about the problem of homelessness to members of Congress. I admire his *dedication to* this cause.

    **A** devotion to      **B** invitation to      **C** distaste for      **D** hesitation with

_____ 6. In her physical therapy sessions, Rachel's *determination* is obvious. She works extremely hard to build strength in her injured leg.

    **A** fear      **B** curiosity      **C** purposefulness      **D** sensitivity

_____ 7. When it comes to his music, Liang has a lot of *discipline*. Even though he sometimes wants to do other things, he spends most of his free time practicing the drums.

    **A** talent      **B** betrayal      **C** tricks      **D** self-control

_____ 8. From mastering Spanish conversation to hiking the Appalachian Trail, Maria has been successful in most of *her endeavors*.

    **A** her friendships         **C** the things she has tried
    **B** the sports she has played      **D** the tests she has taken

_____ 9. Ms. Washington will *enforce* her rule about cell phones in school by patrolling the halls and taking any cell phones she finds to the office.

    **A** change her mind about        **C** make sure everyone obeys
    **B** wish to suspend          **D** choose to ignore

_____ **10.** When the fire was out, the firefighters tried to figure out what had *ignited* it, but they could not find the cause.

    **A** withstood         **B** smothered         **C** started         **D** resisted

_____ **11.** Will's teacher said that she didn't consider "I couldn't think of a good topic" to be a *legitimate* excuse for not doing the assignment but that "I was in the hospital" was.

    **A** reasonable         **B** silly         **C** strange         **D** hopeless

_____ **12.** A pet owner has many joys, but there are also *obligations*, such as providing the pet with food, water, shelter, and affection.

    **A** intentions         **B** duties         **C** restrictions         **D** choices

_____ **13.** If you *persevere*, I believe you will eventually figure out how to solve the problem.

    **A** hesitate         **B** keep trying         **C** give up         **D** guess

_____ **14.** The town committee met to determine its *policy* on recycling, which will govern the way that garbage is collected and reused.

    **A** campaign         **B** desire         **C** safeguard         **D** plan

_____ **15.** Michael loves *politics*; in fact, he wants to become a senator or representative someday.

    **A** journalism    **B** medicine         **C** military matters     **D** government affairs

_____ **16.** Mr. Cunningham does not think our tax system is as fair and efficient as it could be. He believes that the *reform* of tax laws is necessary.

    **A** improvement       **B** circulation        **C** withdrawal       **D** end

_____ **17.** Because Jayda has a great deal of *respect* for her Aunt Kiara, she frequently asks her aunt for advice.

    **A** sympathy         **B** admiration        **C** dislike         **D** bitterness

_____ **18.** Our report must be about *a social issue*, such as poverty or crime. Can you think of any other issues that affect everyone?

    **A** an issue for people in general         **C** an issue for lawyers
    **B** an easy problem                  **D** a matter of friendship

_____ **19.** Even after others criticized him for it, the governor still *upheld* his original position on the housing problem.

    **A** revealed         **B** denied         **C** rejected         **D** supported

_____ **20.** Before the big game, we made a banner that said, "The Victorious Vikings *versus* the Hawks. Goodbye, Hawks!"

    **A** against         **B** for         **C** at         **D** from

**Vocabulary in Context**

# Word Maze

All the words in the box are hidden in the maze. The words are arranged forward, backward, up, down, and diagonally. Put a circle around each word as you find it and cross the word off the list. Different words may overlap and use the same letter.

| attitude | civic | concern | cultured | dedication |
|---|---|---|---|---|
| determination | discipline | endeavor | enforce | ignited |
| legitimate | obligation | persevered | policy | politics |
| reform | respect | social | upheld | versus |

```
A  C  R  D  M  N  R  E  F  O  R  M  P  Q  Z
O  D  I  S  C  I  P  L  I  N  E  M  F  E  T
L  E  C  I  M  A  E  H  N  D  R  T  P  O  U
A  T  T  I  T  U  D  E  G  F  E  P  O  B  V
C  E  T  G  G  V  E  R  S  U  S  O  L  L  L
O  R  S  E  R  N  B  I  C  P  P  L  I  I  E
N  M  E  I  N  T  I  J  K  H  E  I  C  G  G
C  I  F  N  S  F  M  T  L  E  C  T  Y  A  I
E  N  D  E  A  V  O  R  E  L  T  I  G  T  T
R  A  O  M  L  A  C  R  B  D  R  C  H  I  I
N  T  S  O  C  I  A  L  C  K  S  S  T  O  M
T  I  C  I  V  I  C  Q  P  E  M  N  R  N  A
C  O  A  B  D  E  D  I  C  A  T  I  O  N  T
D  N  C  U  L  T  U  R  E  D  D  I  O  T  E
Y  N  P  E  R  S  E  V  E  R  E  D  C  Y  Y
```

Name _____ Date _____

# Standardized Test Practice

Circle the letter of the word that is closest in meaning to the capitalized word.

Always read all the answer choices. Many choices may make sense. Only one answer choice has the same or almost the same meaning as the capitalized word.

_____ **1.** OBLIGATION

  **A** option   **B** objective   **C** characteristic   **D** responsibility

_____ **2.** ATTITUDE

  **A** system   **B** fate   **C** outlook   **D** advantage

_____ **3.** VERSUS

  **A** against   **B** with   **C** for   **D** on

_____ **4.** UPHELD

  **A** destroyed   **B** supported   **C** returned   **D** demolished

_____ **5.** ENDEAVOR

  **A** attempt   **B** failure   **C** habit   **D** success

Circle the letter of the word that is most nearly *opposite* in meaning to the capitalized word.

**TIP**

Always read all the answer choices. Many choices may make sense. Only one answer choice has the opposite or almost the opposite meaning as the capitalized word.

_____ **6.** CULTURED

  **A** crude   **B** polite   **C** refined   **D** respectful

_____ **7.** PERSEVERED

  **A** changed   **B** continued   **C** stopped   **D** ignored

_____ **8.** IGNITED

  **A** extinguished   **B** began   **C** lit   **D** destroyed

_____ **9.** LEGITIMATE

  **A** civic   **B** unreasonable   **C** unhappy   **D** practical

_____ **10.** CONCERN

  **A** care   **B** result   **C** hope   **D** disinterest

# Understanding Related Words

The words in the box are closely related to the vocabulary words. See how many of the words you already know. Use the glossary to find the definitions of unfamiliar words.

| | | | | |
|---|---|---|---|---|
| civilian | culture | enforcement | inform | obligate |
| respectable | respectful | socialize | society | |

Define each italicized word by examining its context, or how it is used in the sentence. Write the definition on the line. Then check your definitions against those in the dictionary.

1. Because he wants to become a police officer, Paulo will study law *enforcement* in college.

   _____

2. Tasting the free sample did not *obligate* us to buy the new brand of crackers, but we bought some because we liked them.

   _____

3. Our drama teacher said our presentation was *respectable* but not excellent.

   _____

4. Mom and Dad both enjoy parties because they like to *socialize*.

   _____

5. You must *inform* Leisha of your decision. If she doesn't know, she will worry.

   _____

6. Alicia is writing an extra-credit report on Japanese *culture*. She will include information about Japanese customs, art, and industry.

   _____

7. After Antonio was discharged from the army, he said he was happy to be a *civilian* again.

   _____

8. *Society* will not tolerate light punishments for people found guilty of serious crimes. People expect these criminals to receive stiff punishment.

   _____

9. Ms. Vásquez said that whispering during the guest speaker's lecture was not a *respectful* way for us to behave.

   _____

**Word Skills**

Name _____ Date _____

# True-False

Decide whether each statement is true or false. Write *T* for True and *F* for False.

_____ 1. A person who loves to read may have a *concern* about the mayor's plan to close the library for three months while repairs are made.

_____ 2. Throwing water on a fire will make it *ignite*.

_____ 3. Ignoring a person is an example of *respectful* behavior.

_____ 4. A *political* ad would probably include a person running for election.

_____ 5. The supervisor called a meeting to *inform* her team about the new policies.

_____ 6. In Japanese *culture*, people remove their shoes when they enter a house.

_____ 7. My uncle is a *civilian* because he is a major in the air force.

_____ 8. Mountain climbers usually have a great deal of *determination*.

_____ 9. A student arriving late to class is *enforcing* the rule against tardiness.

_____ 10. You are not *obligated* to participate in after-school activities.

# Challenge Yourself

Write complete sentences to answer the questions below.

1. Where are two places you might *socialize*?

   _____

   _____

2. Describe two traits, habits, or foods found in a *culture* of your choice.

   _____

   _____

3. If Thomas looks forward to soccer practice every week, how would you describe his *attitude*? Explain.

   _____

   _____

Unit 4
Vocabulary in Context G7, SV 9780547625805

Word Skills

Name _____  Date _____

# The Latin Root *form*

This root comes from the Latin word *forma*, meaning "shape." The word *reform* and the words in the box all contain this root.

| | | | |
|---|---|---|---|
| conform | deformed | inform | transform |
| perform | information | formulate | uniform |

Use your dictionary to learn the meanings of the words. Then write the word from the box that best completes the meaning of each sentence. Some words will be used twice.

_____  1. Did anyone _____ Li of the change in the schedule? If not, please make sure someone calls her.

_____  2. Drivers must _____ to the speed limit restrictions.

_____  3. Picking up the clay pot before it was dry _____ the shape of it.

_____  4. Tutoring sessions and a more positive attitude will help to _____ Ken into a better student.

_____  5. If everyone else is wearing black this year, you can bet I'll wear purple. I hate the idea that everyone has to _____.

_____  6. Scientists are trying to _____ a new type of fuel that will be renewable and inexpensive.

_____  7. Did your coach give you the new _____ for the soccer season?

_____  8. The choir concert is tonight, and Anya is nervous about having to _____ in front of such a large audience.

_____  9. The teacher posted _____ about the upcoming social studies test on her Web site.

_____  10. I am hoping that obedience classes will help _____ my dog from a terror into a well-behaved companion.

_____  11. The shrub's shape was slightly _____ after Tomás fell into it while trying to catch the football.

_____  12. My favorite band will _____ tonight at the Oakley Convention Center.

_____  13. Daniel's _____ is very muddy after playing baseball in the rain yesterday.

Word Skills

# Writing

Think about a time when you tried a difficult task or activity, and write a short description of the endeavor. Were you successful? What made the activity difficult? How did you go about completing the task? Use some vocabulary words from this unit in your writing.

_____

_____

_____

_____

_____

_____

_____

_____

_____

_____

_____

_____

_____

_____

_____

**47**

Writing

# Suppose a Rattlesnake Slithers into Your Life

by James Coomber

Read the selection. Think about the meanings of the **boldfaced** words. Then go back to the selection. Underline the words or sentences that give you a clue to the meaning of each **boldfaced** word.

---

*What would you do if you were suddenly face-to-face with a rattlesnake? This selection offers some helpful hints.*

Many people **loathe** rattlesnakes. Years ago people commonly believed that these and other snakes had the power to **bewitch** people. Some people become frenzied at the thought of even seeing a rattler. Even nature lovers are **compelled** to look out for these creatures. However, knowing a little about these snakes and taking a few sensible precautions will **decrease** your chances of being struck by any poisonous snake.

Rattlers range in size from about a foot in length to over six feet. At the end of the rattler's body is a set of rings. These rings make up the rattle. When the snake is alarmed, the rattle vibrates, causing a warning noise to be **transmitted** a **considerable** distance. Many people believe that you can tell how old a rattlesnake is by the number of rings in its rattle. This is a myth, however. Each time the snake sheds its skin, which can be one to four times a year, a new ring is added to its rattle. These rings are made of protein, much like a fingernail, and can easily be broken off. Therefore, the number of rings does not accurately measure how old the rattlesnake actually is.

Rattlesnakes are called pit vipers because they have two pits under their nostrils that can detect heat. Rattlers use these pits to hunt warm-blooded prey. The pits are so sensitive to heat that rattlers can detect their prey even in complete darkness. They can even sense heat from prey from a distance as great as 30 feet.

pit

Rattlers can be found in nearly all states and in some Canadian provinces. However, most rattlers prefer to live in arid places, such as the western United States and Mexico. Rocky, **isolated** areas are favorite places for rattlers to **lodge**. They may be seen mornings and evenings sunning on rocky ledges. In the heat of midday, they seek out a **haven** from the sun under rocks or in holes. They are most active in the warmer times of the year—spring and early fall. In summer, however, they generally take cover during the day and hunt at night when the temperature is cooler. Rattlers are most active when the air temperature is between 70° and 90°F.

The rattlesnake is in many ways a friend to humans. Although this statement **contradicts** common opinion, the rattler is a big help in controlling the rodent population. The **toxic** venom released by a rattler's bite kills small animals. Rattlers are **competitors** with owls and hawks for rodents such as mice, rats, and gophers. Rodents are often the losers in a **skirmish** with a hungry rattlesnake.

How can you avoid a rattlesnake bite? A few suggestions from **veterans** of the outdoors may help. First, do not run through high grass in areas well suited to rattlesnakes. You might surprise a snake that is otherwise minding its own business. Walking slowly **ensures** ample time for the snake to slither away or **proclaim** its presence.

Although these snakes are very **mobile**, they will not chase you. If you hear a rattle, back up slowly and walk away. Do not run! The snake may have a friend or relative in the area who would **resent** being stepped on as you dash away.

Second, consider your **apparel**, particularly footwear. Snake fangs have occasionally pierced thick Western boots. However, such footgear offers much more protection than ordinary shoes.

Finally, when climbing, look before you reach or step. Rattlers like to rest on rocky ledges. Even if you intended to grab a rock rather than a rattler, the surprised snake might not understand.

Far from seeking a fight with a human, a rattler only strikes to protect itself out of fear. Unless you **violate** the rules, you're not likely to have a painful meeting with a rattler.

# Context Clues

For each sentence write the letter of the word or phrase that is closest in meaning to the word or words in italics. Use context clues to help you choose the correct answer.

_____  1. Members of the soccer team have to buy their own shirts, shorts, socks, and other *apparel*.

    **A** clubs      **B** clothing      **C** accommodations      **D** awards

_____  2. In the fairy tale the old hag was able to *bewitch* small children, making them believe she was a sweet young girl while she led them into the deep woods.

    **A** put a spell over      **B** make fun of      **C** safeguard      **D** scold

_____  3. We couldn't see through the heavy rain and so were *compelled* to stop the car and wait for the weather to clear.

    **A** frightened      **B** helped      **C** forced      **D** unwilling

_____  4. Diane and I are always trying to beat each other in sports. She has always been my greatest *competitor*.

    **A** rival      **B** partner      **C** handicap      **D** coach

_____  5. A robin has *a considerable* number of feathers—about three thousand.

    **A** a constant      **B** a small      **C** an unknown      **D** a large

_____  6. When Derek suddenly became very angry, he *contradicted* his previous statement that he never lost his temper.

    **A** reinforced      **B** revealed      **C** went against      **D** continued

_____  7. As the sun began to set, the temperature in the mountains started to *decrease* quickly.

    **A** improve      **B** get lower      **C** change      **D** warm up

_____  8. The warm cabin was a welcome *haven* from the wet, snowy weather.

    **A** place of shelter      **B** challenge      **C** fantasy      **D** hazard

_____  9. The coach is trying to *ensure* that she will have a winning team by making her players practice every day.

    **A** understand      **B** predict      **C** guarantee      **D** find

_____  10. Kept away from other people so her illness would not spread, the *isolated* patient became very lonely.

    **A** elderly      **B** separated      **C** miraculous      **D** vigorous

    

**11.** Although the twins like most vegetables, they *loathe* lima beans and refuse to eat them.

   **A** hate       **B** prefer       **C** sniff       **D** cook

**12.** Squirrels usually *lodge* in nests made of twigs, but this one lived in the attic of a house.

   **A** have a home       **B** grow       **C** gather       **D** quarrel

**13.** Although the piano has wheels on its legs, no one would think of it as a very *mobile* instrument.

   **A** comfortable       **B** movable       **C** musical       **D** heavy

**14.** Within an hour after the closing of the polls, the candidate for mayor *proclaimed* his victory with a joyful speech. His opponent thought the announcement was made too early.

   **A** gave up       **B** forgot       **C** demonstrated       **D** declared

**15.** Everyone at school *resented* the Gopher football team. Not only did they beat our team regularly, but they made fun of our mascot.

   **A** admired       **C** had bitter feelings toward
   **B** ignored       **D** learned strategies from

**16.** The soldiers had a brief *skirmish* with an enemy patrol. They were lucky no one was hurt in the fight.

   **A** parade       **B** battle       **C** retreat       **D** race

**17.** The scientist discovered that the fish were dying because *toxic* waste had been dumped in the river. The fish had little chance to survive in the deadly mixture.

   **A** transformed       **B** useless       **C** poisonous       **D** floral

**18.** Although Akemi could not speak the language, he still *transmitted* his questions by using sign language and drawing pictures.

   **A** concealed       **B** passed along       **C** transformed       **D** understood

**19.** Because she has been an actress for over thirty years, Ms. Bloom is considered *a veteran* of the Broadway stage.

   **A** an unknown member       **C** a forgotten person
   **B** a first time performer       **D** an experienced performer

**20.** The man believed that his rights as a citizen had been *violated* when he was arrested but not told what he had done wrong.

   **A** transferred       **B** guaranteed       **C** disregarded       **D** protected

**Vocabulary in Context**

Name _____ Date _____

# Fill-Ins

Spell the vocabulary word correctly on the lines to the right of its definition.

1. a brief fight: _s_ ___ ___ ___ ___ ___ _s_ _h_

2. to break a law or rule: ___ _i_ ___ ___ ___ ___ _e_

3. clothing: ___ _p_ _p_ ___ ___ ___ ___

4. experienced people: _v_ ___ ___ ___ _r_ ___ ___ ___

5. sent from one place to another: ___ _r_ ___ ___ _s_ ___ ___ ___ ___ ___ ___

6. forced: ___ ___ _m_ ___ _e_ ___ ___ ___

7. poisonous: ___ ___ _x_ ___ _c_ ___

8. to announce: ___ ___ ___ ___ ___ _a_ _i_ ___

9. to put a spell over; to enchant: ___ _e_ ___ ___ _t_ ___ ___

10. able to be moved: ___ ___ _b_ ___ _l_ ___

11. rivals: _c_ ___ _m_ ___ ___ ___ _t_ ___ ___ ___ ___ ___

12. to hate: ___ ___ ___ _t_ _h_ ___

13. says the opposite: _c_ ___ ___ ___ ___ _r_ ___ ___ ___ ___ ___ ___

14. to live or remain in a place: ___ ___ _d_ _g_ ___

15. to make less: _d_ ___ ___ ___ _e_ _a_ ___ ___

16. guarantees: ___ _n_ ___ ___ ___ _r_ ___ ___

17. a safe shelter: _h_ ___ ___ ___ _n_

18. being apart or alone: ___ _s_ ___ _l_ ___ ___ ___ ___

19. very big: ___ ___ _n_ _s_ ___ ___ ___ ___ ___ ___ ___

20. to feel anger toward: ___ ___ _s_ ___ ___ _t_

Vocabulary in Context

# Finding Examples

Write the letter of the situation that best shows the meaning of the boldfaced word.

_____ **1. apparel**

    **A** Carlos's parents are shopping for a new oven.

    **B** Brendan is sure the answer to the mystery is something obvious.

    **C** Anna is looking for a new dress to wear to her cousin's wedding.

_____ **2. competitor**

    **A** An older club member is Jack's constant rival at swim meets.

    **B** A concert pianist is entertaining his friends at a recital.

    **C** Melina is someone who gives in easily.

_____ **3. haven**

    **A** The captain of the boat looks for a safe harbor during the storm.

    **B** The street becomes very busy during rush hour.

    **C** The fishermen live in a large port city on the New England coast.

_____ **4. skirmish**

    **A** Andrew feels faint and dizzy on even a short boat trip.

    **B** Two hockey players have a brief fight.

    **C** A stream swirls over rocks as it nears the river.

_____ **5. toxic**

    **A** A doctor checks a patient for symptoms of a disease.

    **B** A new medicine fails to cure an illness.

    **C** A chemical waste poisons fish in a river.

_____ **6. transmit**

    **A** You've left your notebook on the school bus.

    **B** You've used a cell phone to talk with someone in England.

    **C** You've enrolled your dog in obedience school.

_____ **7. veteran**

    **A** Mrs. Reyna has been a salesperson for many years.

    **B** Mr. Sylvester has just joined the army.

    **C** Ms. Pirandello is studying to become an animal doctor.

_____ **8. loathe**

    **A** Jake is mildly upset about losing his pen.

    **B** Mitch is willing to forgive Brian and to forget the whole incident.

    **C** Meredith is disgusted with people who mistreat their pets.

_____ **9. mobile**

    **A** The Egyptian pyramids are the graves of ancient rulers.

    **B** The Wongs took their family car on a vacation.

    **C** Brent is very sick and must remain in bed.

Unit 5

Vocabulary in Context G7, SV 9780547625805

Vocabulary in Context

Name _____ Date _____

# Standardized Test Practice

Circle the letter of the word that is most nearly *opposite* in meaning to the capitalized word.

**TIP**
Always read all the answer choices. Many choices may make sense. Only one answer choice has the opposite or almost the opposite meaning as the capitalized word.

1. TRANSMITTED

   **A** propelled     **B** received     **C** required     **D** announced

2. CONSIDERABLE

   **A** sizable     **B** suitable     **C** large     **D** small

3. CONTRADICTS

   **A** challenges     **B** opposes     **C** agrees     **D** detects

4. DECREASE

   **A** propel     **B** demolish     **C** render     **D** expand

5. TOXIC

   **A** repulsive     **B** tasteful     **C** poisonous     **D** healthy

6. MOBILE

   **A** unmovable     **B** movable     **C** fast     **D** slow

7. LOATHE

   **A** hate     **B** demolish     **C** love     **D** neglect

8. VETERAN

   **A** old-timer     **B** beginner     **C** soldier     **D** actor

9. RESENT

   **A** frighten     **B** hate     **C** like     **D** remember

10. VIOLATE

    **A** disregard     **B** offend     **C** break     **D** obey

Name _____ Date _____

# True-False

The words in the box are closely related to the vocabulary words. See how many of the words you already know. Use the glossary to find the definitions of unfamiliar words.

| assure | claim | clamor | compete | competition |
|---|---|---|---|---|
| considers | ensure | increase | isolation | mobility |
| proclamation | resentment | transmission | violation | insurance |

Decide whether each statement is true (**T**) or false (**F**). Write *T* or *F*.

_____ **1.** A traffic *violation* is within the law.

_____ **2.** You can *assure* yourself of not doing poorly in school by studying hard.

_____ **3.** Doctors are not interested in preventing the *transmission* of disease.

_____ **4.** If you have health *insurance*, you would probably expect your medical bills to be paid for you when you are ill.

_____ **5.** A prisoner in *isolation* will have other prisoners for company.

_____ **6.** Good friends usually have *resentment* for each other.

_____ **7.** Voters approved a tax *increase*, so people will be paying less in taxes.

_____ **8.** When the friends faced each other in *competition*, they didn't have to play against each other.

_____ **9.** An athlete who has just begun walking again after recovering from a broken leg probably enjoys his new *mobility*.

_____ **10.** Rival schools with outstanding teams often *compete* for championship trophies.

_____ **11.** If you *claim* this book, you say that it doesn't belong to you.

_____ **12.** When the mayor made a *proclamation* about the new budget, he announced what his plans were for the city finances.

_____ **13.** If a crowd raises a *clamor*, you would expect the noise level to be loud.

_____ **14.** If Grace *considers* her options, she doesn't think about her choices.

_____ **15.** It is important to check the stove before you leave the house to *ensure* that you turned it off.

**55**

Word Skills

# The Latin Root *clam*

The word *proclaim* comes from the Latin word *clamare*, meaning "to shout" or "to cry out." The following words in the box come from this same Latin root.

| claim | clamor | exclaimed | exclamation | proclamation |
|-------|--------|-----------|-------------|--------------|

Look up the meaning of each word in your dictionary. Then use the words in the box to complete the following sentences. Each word will be used twice.

_____  **1.** The king made a _____ that all of his subjects would be treated equally.

_____  **2.** Sheila will attend the court hearing and _____ her share of the estate.

_____  **3.** "Thank goodness you are here at last!" _____ Jordan's worried mother.

_____  **4.** Surprised by the sudden appearance of a detective with a pair of handcuffs, Robert's loud _____ could be heard throughout the theater.

_____  **5.** A loud _____ arose among the audience in the theater when the film abruptly stopped.

_____  **6.** The prospector staked a _____ on the land where he discovered gold.

_____  **7.** The mayor issued a _____ that property taxes would be reduced by 5% in the next year.

_____  **8.** The stands were filled with a loud _____ when the athlete made the last free throw to win the game.

_____  **9.** "I am so happy that we won that game!" _____ the coach with a grin.

_____  **10.** The judge issued a command for order after the witness made an inappropriate _____ in the courtroom.

**Word Skills**

# Writing

Choose one item from each of the columns below. Then write a story based on these three items. Use vocabulary words from this unit in your story.

| **Characters** | **Incidents** | **Conditions** |
|---|---|---|
| • a fierce competitor | • transmitting messages in secret code | • for a ladies' apparel store |
| • the owner of a toxic waste dump | • contradicting everything that was said | • without any decrease in skill |
| • the participants in a brief skirmish | • loathing the present conditions | • toward a quiet haven |
| • a veteran sportswriter | • proclaiming the news | • resenting the other team's skills |
| • a person with a bewitching smile | • compelled to respond | • near a remote hunting lodge |
| • an isolated prisoner on an island | • violating the rules | |

_____

_____

_____

_____

_____

_____

_____

_____

_____

_____

Writing

# The Story of My Life

Read the story. Think about the meanings of the **boldfaced** words. Then go back to the story. Underline the words or sentences that give you a clue to the meaning of each **boldfaced** word.

---

*Though unable to see, hear, or talk, Helen Keller learned to communicate and lead a fulfilling life. Here Helen Keller tells how a teacher, Anne Sullivan, led her to a miraculous breakthrough that changed her life.*

The most important day I remember in all my life is the one on which my teacher, Anne Mansfield Sullivan, came to me. I am filled with wonder when I consider the **immeasurable** contrasts between the two lives which it connects. It was the third of March, 1887, three months before I was seven years old.

On the afternoon of that **eventful** day, I stood on the porch, dumb, expectant. I guessed vaguely from my mother's signs and from the hurrying to and fro in the house that something unusual was about to happen, so I went to the door and waited on the steps. I did not know what the future held of marvel or surprise for me. Anger and **bitterness** had preyed upon me continually for weeks and a deep languor had succeeded this **passionate** struggle.

Have you ever been at sea in a dense fog, when it seemed as if a **tangible** white darkness shut you in, and the great ship, tense and anxious, groped her way toward the shore with plummet and sounding-line, and you waited with beating heart for something to happen? I was like that ship before my education began, only I was without compass or sounding-line and had no way of knowing how near the harbor was. "Light! Give me light!" was the wordless cry of my soul, and the light of love shone on me in that very hour.

I felt approaching footsteps. I stretched out my hand as I supposed to my mother. Someone took it, and I was caught up and held close in the arms of her who had come to reveal all things to me, and, more than all things else, to love me.

The morning after my teacher came she led me into her room and gave me a doll. When I had played with it a little while, Miss Sullivan slowly spelled into my hand the word "d-o-l-l." I was at once interested in this finger play and tried to imitate it. When I finally succeeded in making the letters correctly, I was flushed with childish pleasure and pride. Running downstairs to my mother, I held up my hand and made the letters for doll. I did not know that I was spelling a word or even that words existed; I was simply making my fingers go in monkey-like imitation. In the days that followed, I learned to spell in this **uncomprehending** way a great many words, among them *pin, hat, cup*, and a few verbs like *sit, stand,* and *walk*. But my teacher had been with me several weeks before I understood that everything has a name.

One day, while I was playing with my new doll, Miss Sullivan put a big rag doll into my lap also, spelled "d-o-l-l," and tried to make me understand that "d-o-l-l" applied to both. Earlier in the day we had a **tussle** over the words "m-u-g" and "w-a-t-e-r." Miss Sullivan had tried but I was persistent in confounding the two. In despair she had dropped the subject for the time, only to renew it at the first opportunity. I became impatient at her repeated attempts and, seizing the new doll, I dashed it upon the floor. I was keenly delighted when I felt the fragments of the broken doll at my feet. Neither sorrow nor regret followed my passionate **outburst**. I had not loved the doll. In the still, dark world in which I lived there was no strong **sentiment** of tenderness. I felt my teacher sweep the fragments to one side of the hearth, and I had a sense of satisfaction that the cause of my discomfort was removed. She brought me my hat, and I knew I was going out into the warm sunshine. This thought, if a wordless sensation may be called a thought, made me hop and skip with pleasure. We walked down the path to the well-house, attracted by the fragrance of the honeysuckle with which it was covered. Someone was drawing water and my teacher placed my hand under the spout. As the cool stream gushed over one hand she spelled into the other the word *water*, first slowly, then rapidly. Suddenly I felt a misty consciousness as of something forgotten—a thrill of returning thought; and somehow the mystery of language was revealed to me. I knew then that "w-a-t-e-r" meant the wonderful cool something that was flowing over my hand. That living word awakened my soul, gave it light, hope, joy, set it free!

I left the well-house eager to learn. Everything had a name, and each name gave birth to a new thought. As we returned to the house every object which I touched seemed to quiver with life. That was because I saw everything with the strange, new sight that had come to me. On entering the door I remembered the doll I had broken. I felt my way to the hearth and picked up the pieces. I tried vainly to put them together. Then my eyes filled with tears; for I realized what I had done, and for the first time I felt **repentance** and sorrow.

Vocabulary in Context G7, SV 9780547625805

# Context Clues

Read each pair of sentences. Look for clues to help you complete one of the sentences with a word from the box. Write the word on the line.

| bitterness | outburst | tussle | sentiment | tangible |
|---|---|---|---|---|
| eventful | uncomprehending | immeasurable | passionate | repentance |

**Vocabulary in Context**

_____ 1. Helen Keller's parents never gave up their efforts to help their daughter. They seemed to have _____ love and patience.

_____ 2. The Kellers' life began to improve when they hired Anne Sullivan. The young teacher's arrival marked the beginning of an _____ period in Helen's development.

_____ 3. Miss Sullivan had been blind when she was young and never fully recovered her eyesight. Rather than show any _____ from her childhood experiences, she was loving and eager to help.

_____ 4. Miss Sullivan was an extremely intense teacher. She had a _____ need to help Helen learn.

_____ 5. At first, Miss Sullivan had a difficult time working with Helen. They seemed to get into a _____ about everything.

_____ 6. Helen's parents believed their daughter knew little about the world. But Miss Sullivan sensed that Helen was not as _____ as she seemed.

_____ 7. When Helen had a fit of temper, her parents always gave in to her. Miss Sullivan met each _____ calmly and went on teaching.

_____ 8. Touching Helen's palm, Miss Sullivan traced the letters that spelled the names of things. This _____ spelling brought results.

_____ 9. In time, Helen was sorry for the difficulties she had caused her teacher. She expressed her _____ by hugging Miss Sullivan.

_____ 10. Miss Sullivan loved Helen. Added to this _____ was the one of pride in a job well done.

Name _____  Date _____

# Word Maze

All the words in the box are hidden in the maze. The words are arranged forward, backward, up, down, and diagonally. Put a circle around each word as you find it and cross the word off the list. Different words may overlap and use the same letter.

| bitterness | outburst | tussle | sentiment | tangible |
|---|---|---|---|---|
| eventful | uncomprehending | immeasurable | passionate | repentance |

```
J U O L K N E S R I E U N E D
C O I W Y W V S E M H N O L J
W U E U Y W M E P M I C U K H
Z T T Y W Q S N E E R O T P X
A B A F V M E R N A F M G C C
Y U N Q K G N E T S G P O Q N
K R O A T T T T A U H R C V N
E S I O A X I T N R S E Q J H
V T S M N E M I C A N H L K D
E M S A G L E B E B C E X I Y
N J A U I S N F V L R N Y N E
T Q P D B S T Q S E D D G D D
F L D L L U F R I H I I D L G
U Q K W E T A H V V O N F W H
L D J A F Q D K E B P G D R L
```

www.harcourtschoolsupply.com
© HMH Supplemental Publishers Inc. All rights reserved.

**61**

Unit 6
Vocabulary in Context G7, SV 9780547625805

# Cloze Paragraph

Use the words in the box to complete the paragraph. Then read the paragraph again to be sure it makes sense.

| | | | | |
|---|---|---|---|---|
| uncomprehending | outburst | immeasurable | sentiment | tangible |
| tussle | repentance | bitterness | eventful | passionate |

In an (1) _____ of temper, Helen threw food on the floor. The child seemed

(2) _____ about the proper way to behave at the table. But Miss Sullivan thought

Helen was testing her family. She understood Helen's (3) _____ because she

too had struggled with handicaps in her youth. She knew that Helen's (4) _____

was a result of her inability to communicate. Miss Sullivan was (5) _____ about

helping Helen learn to communicate. With (6) _____ calm, she put the food back

on Helen's plate. Helen felt the food and threw it again. This was a (7) _____ way

of saying, "I dare you to make me eat it!" This (8) _____ with food went back

and forth, making for an (9) _____ dinner hour. Finally, Helen gave in and ate her

supper. Later she apologized, showing her (10) _____.

# Challenge Yourself

1. Name two things that you feel *passionate* about.

   _____


2. Name two kinds of *tussles* that you have seen or been involved in.

   _____


3. Name two situations that would cause you to feel *bitterness*.

   _____

Vocabulary in Context

# Standardized Test Practice

Read each sentence. Pick the word that best completes the sentence. Circle the letter of the correct answer.

> **TIP**
> Before you choose your answer, try reading the sentence with each answer choice. This will help you choose an answer that makes sense.

1. His _____ showed when he lost the contest.

   **A** tangible          **B** immeasurable          **C** bitterness          **D** pleasure

2. Tuesday was a(n) _____ day at work because there were many exciting activities.

   **A** eventful          **B** repentance          **C** immeasurable          **D** tangible

3. The number of stars in the sky is _____.

   **A** repentance          **B** immeasurable          **C** decreasing          **D** counting

4. The sudden _____ broke the silence in the room.

   **A** calming          **B** eventful          **C** outburst          **D** passionate

5. She apologized to me with _____.

   **A** attitude          **B** outburst          **C** repentance          **D** tussle

6. There is strong _____ to save the whales.

   **A** bitterness          **B** disregard          **C** sentiment          **D** curiosity

7. He stared at her in a(n) _____ way because he didn't understand what she was saying.

   **A** bored          **B** uncomprehending          **C** silly          **D** eventful

8. She expressed her ideas with _____ feeling since she felt so strongly about the issue.

   **A** passionate          **B** bitterness          **C** casual          **D** inattentive

9. The fluffy clouds were so close to the ground that they seemed almost _____, as if you could actually touch them.

   **A** annoying          **B** passionate          **C** uncomprehending          **D** tangible

10. The hot-tempered children got into a _____ about whose turn it was to jump on the trampoline.

    **A** sentiment          **B** fair          **C** tussle          **D** classroom

# Understanding Related Words

The words in the box can be related to another form of communication, the Chinese written language. See how many of the words you already know. Use the glossary to find the definitions of unfamiliar words.

| | | | | |
|---|---|---|---|---|
| impractical | signify | imposing | characters | bewildering |
| literal | dialects | identical | figurative | excluding |

In each sentence a word or phrase is underlined. Choose a word from the box that means the same as that word or phrase. Write the word on the line.

1. In Chinese writing, many picture words have a meaning that is <u>beyond the ordinary meaning</u>.

    _____

2. Because there are more than 50,000 of these picture words, written Chinese can be <u>confusing</u> to an outsider.

    _____

3. Most Chinese <u>marks and signs</u> represent ideas.

    _____

4. One sign's <u>actual</u> meaning is "woman in a house." But this sign stands for the word *wife*.

    _____

5. All Chinese can understand this sign, no matter what <u>different forms of the spoken language</u> they use.

    _____

6. If you are used to an alphabet, Chinese writing seems <u>difficult to use</u>, or ineffective.

    _____

7. The letters in an alphabet <u>stand for</u> sounds.

    _____

8. <u>Not counting</u> the fact that a letter may stand for different sounds, it is fairly easy to learn alphabet writing.

    _____

9. Some Chinese people worry about foreigners <u>forcing</u> their customs on China.

    _____

10. With an alphabet, these new words can be written with marks that are <u>exactly alike</u>.

    _____

Word Skills

# Word Origins

Knowing the origin of a word can help you understand its meaning. Read each word origin. Then write each word from the box next to its origin.

| | | | |
|---|---|---|---|
| signify | figurative | bewildering | characters |
| dialects | literal | identical | impractical |

1. from Greek dialektos, conversation _____

2. from Latin idem, the same _____

3. from Old English wildernesse, wild place _____

4. from Latin signum, sign _____

5. from Latin littera, letter _____

6. from Greek praktos, to be done _____

7. from Latin figura, a form or shape _____

8. from Greek kharox, a pointed stake _____

# Understanding Multiple-Meaning Words

The word in the box has more than one meaning. Look for clues in each sentence to tell which meaning is being used. Write the letter of the meaning next to the correct sentence.

> **character**
> **a.** moral strength or weakness
> **b.** letter, mark, or sign
> **c.** person or animal in a play, poem, or story
> **d.** person who attracts attention by being different or odd

1. _____ There are thousands of written *characters* in Chinese.

2. _____ Their odd hairstyles make Bo and Mo real *characters*.

3. _____ Most of the *characters* in the book are realistic.

4. _____ The *characters* of heroes and cowards are different.

# The Prefixes *im-* and *un-*

The prefixes *im-* and *un-* generally mean "not." Other prefixes that often mean "not" are *in-*, *il-*, *ir-*, and *non-*.

Add either *im-* or *un-* to the words below. Write the newly formed word and then write the meaning of the new word, using a dictionary to check your work.

**1.** comprehending

New Word: _____

Definition: _____

**2.** practical

New Word: _____

Definition: _____

**3.** measurable

New Word: _____

Definition: _____

**4.** aware

New Word: _____

Definition: _____

**5.** common

New Word: _____

Definition: _____

**6.** probable

New Word: _____

Definition: _____

**7.** mindful

New Word: _____

Definition: _____

**8.** movable

New Word: _____

Definition: _____

**Word Skills**

# Writing

Helen Keller was both blind and deaf. Think about your five senses (sight, hearing, smell, touch, and taste). Which one of these senses do you appreciate most?

Write a paragraph describing this sense. Tell how the use of the sense makes your world complete. Use some vocabulary words from this unit in your writing.

_____

_____

_____

_____

_____

_____

_____

_____

_____

_____

_____

_____

_____

_____

_____

**Writing**

# Setting Her Own Course

Read the selection below. Think about the meanings of the **boldfaced** words. Then go back to the selection. Underline the words or sentences that give you a clue to the meaning of each **boldfaced** word.

---

*Running a marathon can be a grueling challenge. Read this story about a runner who met the challenge and beat it!*

In a **marathon**, runners travel more than twenty-six miles over open country. A top-flight runner can complete this long-distance race in about two and one-half hours, but it is **agonizing** for even an experienced runner. Runners become exhausted, they develop muscle cramps and soreness, and they may collapse from dizziness or fatigue. **Adverse** weather conditions—wind, rain, and extreme cold or heat—can add to the challenge. Often, only people with a special **aptitude**, or natural ability, choose to run marathons. The difficulties **dishearten** many athletes. However, marathon runners are not easily discouraged.

Cathy O'Brien of New Hampshire has been competing in long-distance races since she was thirteen. From the beginning, she showed her strength and energy by running the whole course. She had the **stamina** to run long races. She also had the desire to **excel**, to set new time records.

O'Brien competed in the first women's Olympic Marathon Trials when she was only sixteen. By far the youngest runner, she surprised everyone by finishing ninth in a field of more than two hundred. Four years later, she placed third in the U.S. trials and went on to the Olympics in Seoul, Korea, where she finished fortieth. In her third try at the Olympics, she finished second in the U.S. trials and tenth in the world. She paid a heavy price for her achievement, though. She competed with a hamstring injury. After the race, the pain in her leg was **acute**. It hurt so much that she couldn't run a step for four months. She trained for the 1996 Olympics in Atlanta, Georgia, but she was not able to compete in the U.S. trials. Yet she still runs. O'Brien competed in long-distance races in 2003.

Ordinarily O'Brien is an easy-going person, but in a race she is different. She is an **aggressive** runner. She loves to compete, and she runs to win. She decides which races she will enter and how she will train. Praise is not important to her. Winning the **acclaim** of everyone is not why she runs.

Describing her feelings about running, O'Brien says, "I come off as a mellow person. Some might think I don't care. But once the starting gun goes off, I become a different person. I don't run marathons because it's a job or because that's what others have done. I've been doing it so long that the marathon's like another part of me."

# Context Clues

Meanings for the vocabulary words are given below. Go back to the selection and read each sentence that contains a vocabulary word. If you still cannot tell the meaning, look for clues in the sentences that come before and after the one with the vocabulary word. Write each word in front of its meaning.

| aptitude | agonizing | aggressive | acclaim | marathon |
|----------|-----------|------------|---------|----------|
| stamina  | adverse   | dishearten | acute   | excel    |

_____ **1.** an extremely long race or contest

_____ **2.** a natural talent, ability, or capacity

_____ **3.** be better or do better than others

_____ **4.** physical strength or endurance

_____ **5.** enthusiastic approval; high praise

_____ **6.** not favorable; harmful

_____ **7.** sharp and severe

_____ **8.** cause to lose hope; discourage

_____ **9.** causing great pain and suffering

_____ **10.** energetic and forceful

# Challenge Yourself

**1.** Name two sports in which you need *stamina*.

_____

**2.** Name two problems that you consider to be *acute* in today's world.

_____

**3.** Name two situations that can *dishearten* a student.

_____

**4.** Name two activities that you would like to *excel* in.

_____

# Crossword Puzzle

Use the words in the box and the clues to complete the crossword puzzle.

| acclaim | acute | agonizing | aggressive | aptitude |
|---------|-------|-----------|------------|----------|
| adverse | dishearten | excel | marathon | stamina |

**Vocabulary in Context**

### Across

**1.** strength and endurance

**4.** to do something very well

**5.** an extremely long race or contest

**7.** difficult or unfavorable

**8.** causing great pain or suffering

**9.** to discourage someone

**10.** extreme; difficult or severe

### Down

**2.** recognition or approval

**3.** bold; forceful

**6.** natural talent or ability

www.harcourtschoolsupply.com
70
Unit 7
Vocabulary in Context G7, SV 9780547625805

# Word Origins

Knowing the origin of a word can help you understand its meaning. Read each word origin. Then write each word from the box next to its origin.

| acclaim | adverse | acute | agonizing |
|---------|---------|-------|-----------|
| aggressive | excel | aptitude | |

1. from the Latin excellere, to raise up _____

2. from the Latin acutus, sharp _____

3. from the Greek agonia, struggle _____

4. from the Latin aptitudo, fitness _____

5. from the Latin avertere, turn around _____

6. from the Latin aggressio, going toward _____

7. from the Latin acclamare, to shout applause _____

# Connotations

Some words are very close in meaning, yet there is a small difference between them. The words suggest slightly different things. That is, the words have different **connotations**. Read each sentence below. Choose a word from the box that has a slightly different connotation from the underlined word. Write the vocabulary word on the line.

| dishearten | stamina | acclaim | aggressive | marathon |
|------------|---------|---------|------------|----------|

1. He has the ability to run well, but he may lack the _____ to make it through the whole race.

2. She is vigorous and certain of her goal, but she is not _____ enough to pursue it.

3. It was a tough contest, but not long enough or hard enough to be called a _____.

4. Losing the race upset her, but she will not let this setback _____ her.

5. They had hoped to win national _____, but they had to be satisfied with a round of applause from the audience.

Name _____ Date _____

# Word Groups

Read each pair of words. Think about how they are alike. Write the word from the box that best completes each group.

| | | | | |
|---|---|---|---|---|
| dishearten | aggressive | acclaim | marathon | stamina |
| adverse | aptitude | acute | excel | |

**1.** unfavorable, harmful, _____

**2.** ability, knack, _____

**3.** exceed, outdo, _____

**4.** energetic, forceful, _____

**5.** strength, endurance, _____

**6.** severe, extreme, _____

**7.** discourage, unnerve, _____

**8.** applause, praise, _____

**9.** relay, sprint, _____

# Antonyms

Remember that **antonyms** are words with opposite meanings. Match the words in the box with their antonyms below. Write each word on the line.

| | | | |
|---|---|---|---|
| agonizing | aggressive | acclaim | dishearten |
| adverse | stamina | acute | excel |

**1.** dull: _____

**2.** encourage: _____

**3.** painless: _____

**4.** timid: _____

**5.** fail: _____

**6.** disapproval: _____

**7.** tiredness: _____

**8.** favorable: _____

Vocabulary in Context

# Standardized Test Practice

Write the letter of the word that best completes each sentence in the space provided.

Vocabulary in Context

**TIP**

Before you choose an answer, try reading the sentences with each answer choice. This will help you choose an answer that makes sense.

_____ 1. If you **excel** in something, you do _____ in it.

    **A** poorly      **B** well      **C** average      **D** nothing

_____ 2. If you have an **aptitude** for a sport, you should _____ it.

    **A** avoid      **B** watch      **C** play      **D** ignore

_____ 3. A _____ is an **adverse** weather condition.

    **A** light breeze      **B** blizzard      **C** misty rain      **D** warm temperature

_____ 4. An **acute** pain would be very _____.

    **A** dull      **B** mild      **C** brief      **D** intense

_____ 5. A rainy day might **dishearten** someone going to a _____.

    **A** picnic      **B** movie      **C** mall      **D** library

_____ 6. A **marathon** runner runs for _____ distances.

    **A** long      **B** frequent      **C** short      **D** easy

_____ 7. **Acclaim** for a job well done is usually in the form of _____.

    **A** concern      **B** criticism      **C** resentment      **D** praise

_____ 8. An **agonizing** disease is one that is quite _____.

    **A** common      **B** unusual      **C** painful      **D** distinct

_____ 9. To increase your **stamina**, you must _____ a lot.

    **A** exercise      **B** smile      **C** study      **D** question

_____ 10. **Aggressive** people often do _____ they have to.

    **A** less than      **B** more than      **C** the same as      **D** nothing

# Analogies

An **analogy** compares two pairs of words. The relationship between the first pair of words is the same as the relationship between the second pair of words. For example: *Finger* is to *hand* as *toe* is to *foot*. Use the words in the box to complete the following analogies.

| aptitude | aggression | marathon | frustrate | acute |
|----------|------------|----------|-----------|-------|

1. *Tall* is to *short* as *mild* is to _____.

2. *Giggle* is to *chuckle* as *discourage* is to _____.

3. *Sharp* is to *blunt* as *sprint* is to _____.

4. *Slick* is to *slippery* as *talent* is to _____.

5. *Idleness* is to *inactivity* as *destructiveness* is to _____.

# Find the Word

Read each sentence. Look for clues to help you complete each sentence with a word from the box. Write the word on the line.

| agony | acclamation | tenacity | avert | excellence |
|-------|-------------|----------|-------|------------|

1. The volleyball team received much _____ when they won the state championship.

2. At the end of the year, Ms. Pérez was presented with an award for _____ in teaching.

3. When Martin and Lilly see blood, they _____ their eyes.

4. Erin sprained her ankle when she tumbled down the steep hill, so she was in

   _____ walking back to camp.

5. Even though he was in last place, Ryan ran the last two miles with _____.

Vocabulary in Context G7, SV 9780547625805

**Word Skills**

Name _____ Date _____

# Word Clues

Read each sentence below. Look for clues in each sentence to help you define each underlined word.

1. My brother has an <u>aptitude</u> for playing the guitar, and he hopes to make music his career.

   *Aptitude* means _____.

2. When Maria broke her leg, she was in <u>agony</u>.

   *Agony* means _____.

3. Paulo took out his <u>aggression</u> in the gym by punching a boxing bag.

   *Aggression* means _____.

4. Our city has received <u>acclamation</u> for the new recycling program we recently implemented.

   *Acclamation* means _____.

5. I have been training for six months so that I can run in the <u>marathon</u> in April.

   *Marathon* means _____.

6. Despite the rainy weather, my dad showed great <u>tenacity</u> when putting up the fence in our backyard.

   *Tenacity* means _____.

7. The cars will avoid the parade because the police officer will <u>avert</u> traffic to another street.

   *Avert* means _____.

8. I do not want to <u>frustrate</u> you, but you have only two minutes to finish the test.

   *Frustrate* means _____.

9. The pain in his heel was <u>acute</u> after he stepped on the sharp piece of glass.

   *Acute* means _____.

10. Naomi's <u>excellence</u> in mathematics earned her a scholarship.

   *Excellence* means _____.

Name _____     Date _____

# Synonym or Antonym?

Each numbered word below is either a synonym or an antonym of the underlined word in the sentence. Write *S* for synonym or *A* for antonym.

Maya has shown great <u>aptitude</u> for swimming, and she is in training for the Olympics.

_____ 1. talent

_____ 2. inability

_____ 3. skill

Despite the <u>agony</u> of having sprained her ankle, Arianna kept running to finish the race.

_____ 4. peace

_____ 5. pain

_____ 6. torture

The <u>aggression</u> of the other team caused the referee to call many fouls against them.

_____ 7. hostility

_____ 8. assault

_____ 9. shyness

_____ 10. passivity

I don't wish to <u>frustrate</u> you, but 75 people are trying out for the soccer team, and there are only 12 open spots.

_____ 11. discourage

_____ 12. motivate

Her artistic <u>excellence</u> could be seen in her paintings.

_____ 13. achievement

_____ 14. failure

_____ 15. success

The pain in his head was <u>acute</u>, so we took him to the doctor for an X-ray.

_____ 16. intense

_____ 17. dull

_____ 18. slight

The neighbors were able to <u>avert</u> a crime by calling the police when they saw an unknown person in our garage.

_____ 19. stop

_____ 20. aid

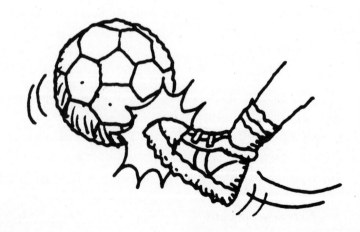

Word Skills

# Writing

Do you have a favorite sport that you feel strongly about, as Cathy O'Brien does about running the marathon? Or do you have a favorite hobby or free-time activity?

Write about your favorite sport or other activity. Tell what it involves, why you like it, how you try to improve, and what your goals are. Use some vocabulary words from this unit in your writing.

_____

_____

_____

_____

_____

_____

_____

_____

_____

_____

_____

_____

_____

Writing

# Quake, Tremble, and Roll

Read the selection below. Think about the meanings of the **boldfaced** words. Then go back to the selection. Underline the words or sentences that give you a clue to the meaning of each **boldfaced** word.

---

An earthquake sends no warning. It is one of nature's terrifying surprises. It begins with a **tremor**, a shaking, rolling motion underfoot. It might even be mistaken for the rumbling of a truck. During the next few seconds, buildings sway and windows shatter, disturbed by the sudden shock to Earth's surface.

Scientists say there may be as many as a million earthquakes in a single year. Most of them are not **destructive** and cause no damage. However, the **severity** of others is much greater. Earthquakes can set whole cities on fire, bring buildings crashing down, and cause many deaths.

Scientists have a theory involving plates that explains why earthquakes happen. According to this theory, there are a number of huge plates, or great rigid masses, under the earth's crust. These plates are in slow but continuous motion. They travel about one-half inch to four inches a year. Because the plates are not traveling in the same direction, sometimes two of them collide. When that happens, they **exert** pressure against each other, creating **friction**. Friction produces strain on the rocks at the plate's edge. At the **crucial** moment that the strain becomes too great, a sudden break occurs. It causes shock waves that move in all directions. The shock waves reach the surface, and the earth begins to shake and tremble.

The movement of the plates is also responsible for the creation of some mountains. When one plate is forced upward by another plate, it **disrupts** the earth above, tearing it apart. The earth that is pushed upward becomes a new mountain.

The plates do not have the same outlines as landmasses on Earth. Each plate goes beyond the **contour** of the continents, out underneath the oceans. In fact, the plates cannot even be identified with a specific **hemisphere**, or half of the globe. In other words, the plates have shapes and movements all their own. They move under Earth's crust year after year. Yet these movements are not **audible** to the human ear. It is only when we hear the commotion created by an earthquake, feel the tremors, and see the destruction that we are reminded of the presence of the plates.

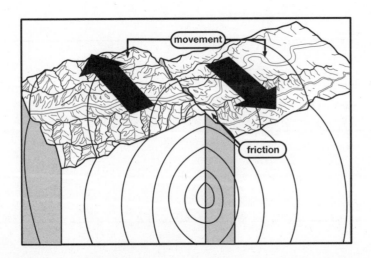

Name _____     Date _____

# Context Clues

Read each pair of sentences. Look for clues to help you complete one of the sentences with a word from the box. Write the word on the line.

| destructive | severity | friction | audible | disrupts |
| hemisphere | crucial | contour | tremor | exert |

Vocabulary in Context

1. Near dawn on April 18, 1906, certain plates underneath San Francisco began rubbing together. This

   _____ was so powerful that it caused the land above to split open.

2. As it began below the crust of the earth, the earthquake was silent. But moments later, the sounds of

   windows breaking and buildings falling were _____.

3. Cliffs fell into the ocean, and mountains filled small valleys. The _____ of
   the land changed for hundreds of miles all around.

4. The people of San Francisco were not aware that morning of the rolling and shaking far beneath their

   homes. When the strongest _____ hit the city, most people were still asleep.

5. The quake was strong enough to cause tremendous damage. Its _____ was
   such that the city hall collapsed into a pile of stone and brick, leaving only the frame standing.

6. Trains and trolleys and gas and water service were all stopped. A disaster like this

   _____ many public services.

7. Gas leaks caused fires, but water would not flow from fire hydrants because the water pipes had

   broken, too. It was _____ that water be found somewhere.

8. Fire raged for four days and destroyed 28,000 buildings in San Francisco. This frightening fact shows

   just how _____ a major earthquake can be.

9. Earthquakes can happen anywhere. Several of the most deadly have occurred in cities in the

   western _____.

10. Earthquakes _____ great pressure on tall buildings. Architects are trying to
    design buildings that will remain standing during a major quake.

# Word Maze

All the words in the list below are hidden in the maze. The words are arranged forward, backward, up, down, and diagonally. Put a circle around each word as you find it and cross the word off the list. Different words may overlap and use the same letter.

| destructive | severity | friction | audible | disrupts |
|-------------|----------|----------|---------|----------|
| hemisphere  | crucial  | contour  | tremor  | exert    |

```
E  U  I  L  H  P  V  D  Y  I  B  M  S
Q  V  C  O  E  B  F  E  R  V  D  P  E
N  U  A  Z  M  S  R  S  O  C  M  E  V
T  H  U  E  I  T  I  T  M  R  V  J  E
T  R  D  D  S  P  C  R  E  U  K  R  R
Z  D  I  U  P  U  T  U  R  C  U  U  I
Q  D  B  Z  H  R  I  C  T  I  L  O  T
T  G  L  D  E  S  O  T  O  A  N  T  Y
W  N  E  X  R  I  N  I  B  L  M  N  A
Z  M  E  K  E  D  O  V  T  O  T  O  K
Z  R  R  S  U  Q  T  E  C  H  R  C  Y
T  G  H  B  G  G  H  X  R  A  I  J  E
F  E  V  L  H  E  U  S  S  Z  I  F  C
```

Vocabulary in Context G7, SV 9780547625805

Name _____ Date _____

# Find the Word

Read each sentence. Look for clues to help you complete each sentence with a word from the box. Write the word on the line.

| | | | | |
|---|---|---|---|---|
| destructive | severity | friction | audible | disrupts |
| hemisphere | crucial | contour | tremor | exert |

1. If you lived in Australia, you would live in the southern _____.

2. An earthquake is a _____ force that can cause severe damage to properties.

3. The _____ of an earthquake depends on the strength of the quake and how much damage it causes.

4. An earthquake is caused by _____ when Earth's plates collide.

5. Some earthquakes start out with silent movements, but then their power becomes

   _____ when windows shatter and buildings collapse.

6. It is _____ that people remain calm when earthquakes occur; if people panic, then they can put themselves in jeopardy.

7. The _____ of the landforms can change after an earthquake; mountains and valleys can form as a result of the earth's movements.

8. The earthquake was a small one, and only a slight _____ was felt by the people in the city.

9. An earthquake _____ the landforms by tearing apart the surface of the earth's crust.

10. Earthquakes are caused when Earth's plates _____ pressure against each other.

# Challenge Yourself

1. Name two of Earth's natural forces that can be *destructive*.

   _____

2. Describe two forces of nature that are *audible*.

   _____

# Tangled-Up Words

In the following passage, the underlined words do not make sense. But they sound similar to a word in the box. Study the context in which the underlined words appear. For each word, find the word in the box that should be used in its place. Write the correct word on the numbered line.

| destructive | severity | friction | audible | disrupted |
|---|---|---|---|---|
| hemisphere | crucial | contour | tremor | exert |

Last summer my family decided to vacation in California. What an adventure—we arrived just in time for an earthquake!

Actually, we didn't even know an earthquake was occurring at first. We felt a (1) tractor, but we thought the shaking was from all the trucks passing outside. (We had begged to stay by the ocean, where the sound of the waves would be (2) edible, but instead we were by a freeway.) Then a jolt of greater (3) serenity hit. I was doing so much rolling and shaking, I felt like the left (4) atmosphere of my brain had traded places with the right!

About this time we decided it was (5) cruelty for us to find a shelter where we would be safer. I was so afraid; I had to (6) exit all my strength just to make myself walk. I was sure that when we got outside, there would be fallen buildings, great holes in the earth, and other signs of the (7) decorative power of this earthquake.

What a shock! There was hardly any damage. Where I had expected the (8) contest of the land to have been altered violently, it looked just the same as when we arrived. We asked the motel owner if he was concerned, but he said this earthquake was just a minor one. "Just a little (9) fiction between the plates!" he laughed.

Well, two jolts in one day was enough for my family! We might seem like Eastern dudes from the days of the old West, but we checked out of that motel, climbed in our car, and headed for quiet ground. That earthquake may not have disturbed the natives, but it sure (10) erupted our vacation!

1. _____
2. _____
3. _____
4. _____
5. _____

6. _____
7. _____
8. _____
9. _____
10. _____

Name _____  Date _____

# Rewriting Sentences

Rewrite each sentence using one of the words from the box.

| exert | tremor | friction | contour | hemisphere |
| --- | --- | --- | --- | --- |

1. This half of Earth has active earthquake areas.

_____

2. An earthquake can change the outline of a shore.

_____

3. We felt the first shaking, rolling motion.

_____

4. The rubbing of the giant plates was building rapidly.

_____

5. The plates put pressure on one another.

_____

# Connotations

Some words are very close in meaning, yet there is a small difference between them. The words suggest slightly different things. Remember that this means the words have different **connotations**. Read each sentence below. Choose a word in the box that has a slightly different connotation from the underlined word. Write the vocabulary word on the line.

| crucial | destructive | disrupts | severity |
| --- | --- | --- | --- |

1. An earthquake can be harmful to a whole city. _____

2. An earthquake's harshness determines how much damage is done. _____

3. It is important that every city have a disaster plan. _____

4. An earthquake interrupts many needed services. _____

Vocabulary in Context G7, SV 9780547625805

# Standardized Test Practice

Write the letter of the word that best completes each sentence in the space provided.

**TIP**

Before you choose an answer, try reading the sentences with each answer choice. This will help you choose an answer that makes sense.

1. The wildfire burned acres of forest and homes. The fire was very _____.
   A helpful     C destructive
   B crucial     D inferior

2. Alice had an acute pain in her side. She had to go to the doctor because of its _____.
   A motion     C weight
   B tremor     D severity

3. The explosion caused the house to shake. One wall cracked from this _____.
   A tremor     C hemisphere
   B paint     D sound

4. Jan wants to go to the school dance. She will _____ pressure on me to let her go.
   A excel     C disrupt
   B feel     D exert

5. This road follows the shoreline. We can see the _____ of the coast ahead.
   A tremor     C contour
   B city     D lighting

6. When Jordan visits, he wants to go places. He is fun, but he _____ our routine.
   A prolongs     C disappoints
   B disrupts     D exerts

7. Most of South America is below the equator. It is in the southern _____.
   A hemisphere     C friction
   B atmosphere     D district

8. The plates below Earth's surface may rub against each other. This _____ can cause an earthquake.
   A ripple     C friction
   B contest     D hemisphere

9. If Jim wants to make the Olympic team, he must win the race. This is a _____ win for his career.
   A modern     C destructive
   B unusual     D crucial

10. The music was very soft, but it was still _____ to me.
    A serious     C silky
    B audible     D dangerous

# Word Descriptions

Read each word description. Then write the word from the box that best fits each description. Use your dictionary if you need help.

| structure | frayed | auditory | biosphere | essential | tsunami |
|-----------|--------|----------|-----------|-----------|---------|

1. You might use this word to describe a place where animals and plants live.

_____

2. Something that is extremely important can be described using this word.

_____

3. This word describes the process of hearing.

_____

4. This is a long sea wave caused by an earthquake or volcanic eruption.

_____

5. Something that is formed, arranged, or organized can be described as this.

_____

6. This word describes how something, such as the edges of fabric, becomes worn away from rubbing.

_____

# Word Origins

Knowing the origin of a word can help you understand its meaning. Read each word origin. Then write each word from the box next to its origin.

| biosphere | structure | frayed | auditory |
|-----------|-----------|--------|----------|

1. from the Latin verb audire, meaning "to hear" _____

2. from the Greek root sphaira, meaning "ball" _____

3. from the Latin root struct, meaning "to build" _____

4. from the Latin root fricare, meaning "rub" _____

Name _____ Date _____

# Sentence Completion

Write the word from the list below that best completes the meaning of the sentence.

| | | | | |
|---|---|---|---|---|
| structure | stern | frayed | audible | disrupts |
| biosphere | crucial | contour | tsunami | intensity |

_____ 1. The _____ of the wave allowed me to ride my surfboard all the way to the shore.

_____ 2. The _____ is where all life exists.

_____ 3. The barking dog next door _____ my sleep every Saturday morning.

_____ 4. Through much use over the years, the edges of the tablecloth have become _____.

_____ 5. The _____ of my essay will show the advantages and disadvantages of having a class pet.

_____ 6. The sound of the train whistle in the distance was barely _____.

_____ 7. The coach gave a _____ warning to her players about bad sportsmanship.

_____ 8. It is _____ that you practice several times this week so that you will do well in the recital on Saturday.

_____ 9. Relief workers arrived to help the survivors of the devastating _____.

_____ 10. When the river flooded, the _____ of its banks changed dramatically.

# Writing

Imagine that a magazine has hired you to write about your experiences during a disaster. Think of a natural disaster you are familiar with or an imagined one.

Write an article about your experiences, real or made-up ones. Tell when each event happened and how you and others dealt with emergencies and fears. Use some vocabulary words from this unit in your writing.

_____

_____

_____

_____

_____

_____

_____

_____

_____

_____

_____

_____

_____

Writing

# Wonder Woman

Read the selection. Think about the meanings of the **boldfaced** words. Then go back to the selection. Underline the words or sentences that give you a clue to the meaning of each **boldfaced** word.

---

Kitty O'Neil inches cautiously across the roof of an apartment building as a would-be killer forces her toward the edge. Suddenly, she slips and disappears over the side!

It's all in a day's work for Kitty O'Neil. She is a stuntwoman who makes her living doing hazardous tricks and **acrobatics** in the movies. In the scene just described, she is taking the place of an actress who could not do these things. Dangerous scenes in movies are almost always performed by stuntpeople. During these scenes, they assume the **identity** of the star. They wear the same clothing and hairstyle. They are matched so their height and weight are the same, too.

O'Neil first became interested in doing stunts when she married a stuntman, Duffy Hambleton. She asked him to teach her what he knew. Soon she was learning to fall, to fake fights, and to roll cars. Within a few years, she was a popular stuntwoman in Hollywood.

Being a successful stuntwoman requires great **coordination**. O'Neil must be in top form and able to move well. Even so, she wears a harness in stunts where she falls off a roof.

O'Neil does a lot of car and motorcycle stunts. During a chase scene in one movie, she rolled a car over three times. Such **antics** take plenty of physical skill and training. They also require great **agility**. But O'Neil can deliver. Her movements are quick and easy and right on target. Kitty O'Neil is an **ace**, tops in her field.

In her private life, O'Neil has known real **adversity**. When she was four months old, she got measles, mumps, and smallpox all at the same time. She had an alarmingly high fever, and no doctor was available to care for her. After several days, her temperature did come down, but the damage was done. O'Neil had lost her hearing.

O'Neil has never let this **disability** become an obstacle to achievement. In fact, she has always looked at her deafness as a challenge. Besides being a stuntwoman, Kitty O'Neil is also a race-car driver. She finds this sport exciting and **exhilarating**. She holds twenty-nine world speed records.

Kitty O'Neil doesn't see herself as Wonder Woman. But her **assurance** and confidence have helped her achieve many goals.

# Context Clues

Read each pair of sentences. Look for clues to help you complete the second sentence with a word from the box. Write the word on the line.

| identity | acrobatics | adversity | disability | coordination |
|----------|-----------|-----------|-----------|--------------|
| exhilarating | antics | ace | agility | assurance |

1. Kitty O'Neil is deaf. But she has never let this _____ stop her from achieving her goals.

2. She performs hazardous stunts in the movies. She is very good at these _____.

3. O'Neil often takes the place of the leading actress. She assumes the _____ of that star while doing dangerous stunts.

4. A stunt person must be able to move with grace and balance. It takes _____ to avoid injury.

5. A good stunt person must be able to move quickly and easily while performing stunts. O'Neil has

   the _____ that is needed to be one of the best stuntwomen in the movies.

6. O'Neil also believes in herself and in her abilities. That _____ has contributed to her success.

7. Such qualities have helped O'Neil to face difficult trials in her life. She has not let

   _____ defeat her.

8. Instead, O'Neil strives to be the best at whatever she does. She is an _____ stuntwoman and a top race-car driver.

9. Rolling a car is deadly serious business to O'Neil. She does not consider such activities to be just

   pranks or _____.

10. Skilled people like Kitty O'Neil find excitement in racing a car at top speeds. They find the

    experience _____ because they are in control.

# Word Map

Use the vocabulary words in the box to complete the word map about stunt performers. Add other words that you know to each group.

| acrobatics | agility | coordination |
|------------|---------|--------------|
| exhilarating | ace | antics |

## What Stunt Performers Do

1. _____
2. _____
3. _____
4. _____
5. _____

## Qualities of Stunt Performers

1. _____
2. _____
3. _____
4. _____
5. _____

## STUNT PERFORMERS

## Terms That Describe Stunt Performers

1. _____
2. _____
3. _____
4. _____
5. _____

## How Audiences Might Describe Stunt Performances

1. _____
2. _____
3. _____
4. _____
5. _____

# Crossword Puzzle

Use the words in the box and the clues to complete the crossword puzzle.

| identity | acrobatics | adversity | disability | coordination |
|----------|-----------|-----------|-----------|--------------|
| exhilarating | antics | ace | agility | assurance |

## Across

1. all the things that make a specific person different from others
3. a person who is an expert in a specific activity
5. a lack of ability to do a certain thing
6. stunts that require strength and good balance
8. smooth and skillful body movements
9. stunts or tricks

## Down

2. thrilling or exciting
3. confidence
4. trouble or difficulty
7. the ability to move quickly and easily

# Connotations

Some words are very close in meaning, yet there is a small difference between them. The words suggest slightly different things. This means the words have different **connotations**. Read each question below. Choose the underlined word that is the more appropriate answer to each question. Write the word on the line.

1. Who would perform a plane stunt with greater ease—a <u>master</u> or an <u>ace</u>?

   _____

2. Which is harder to overcome— an <u>adversity</u> or a <u>challenge</u>?

   _____

3. Which actions—<u>tricks</u> or <u>antics</u>—are more likely to cause laughter?

   _____

4. Which would an Olympic gymnast do in a competition—<u>stunts</u> or <u>acrobatics</u>?

   _____

5. Which would be the better word to describe a trip in a hot-air balloon—<u>exhilarating</u> or <u>lively</u>?

   _____

6. Which would a spy work harder to hide—his <u>identity</u> or his <u>appearance</u>?

   _____

# Word Pairs

Words with similar parts may have related meanings. Study each word pair. Think about how the meanings of the words are alike. Check the meanings in your dictionary. Then write a sentence for each word.

1. assure–assurance

   _____

   _____

2. disable–disability

   _____

   _____

3. agile–agility

   _____

   _____

Vocabulary in Context

# Standardized Test Practice

Choose the word or words that best take the place of the boldfaced word. Write the letter of your choice in the space provided.

**TIP**

This test shows how well you understand the meaning of the words. Think about the meaning of the boldfaced word before you choose your answer.

_____ 1. My son loved the clown's **antics**. He was the funniest performer in the circus.

    **A** outburst        **B** costume        **C** pranks        **D** props

_____ 2. Holly has a **disability** in school. She has difficulty reading.

    **A** disadvantage        **B** headache        **C** trial        **D** blindness

_____ 3. A gymnast must have excellent **coordination**. It takes grace and skill to maintain such balance.

    **A** muscle control        **B** concentration        **C** courage        **D** breathing patterns

_____ 4. She kept her **identity** a secret. She did not want people to ask her for an autograph.

    **A** travel plans        **C** family relationships
    **B** name and appearance        **D** bank account

_____ 5. I could watch the ice skaters for hours. Their **acrobatics** delight me.

    **A** accents        **B** silly jokes        **C** dangerous acts        **D** gymnastic feats

_____ 6. This test will measure your **agility**. You must run the course and jump over objects of different heights.

    **A** ability to plan races        **C** quick and easy movements
    **B** knowledge of colors        **D** patience and confidence

_____ 7. Lionel entered the contest with a great deal of **assurance**. He felt certain that he would win.

    **A** concern        **B** curiosity        **C** confidence        **D** compromise

_____ 8. Cara is an **ace**. She can make an old engine work like a new one.

    **A** expert        **B** engineer        **C** artist        **D** athlete

_____ 9. It was an **exhilarating** day. Everyone was amazed at the view from the top of the mountain.

    **A** expressive        **B** disappointing        **C** annoying        **D** exciting

_____ 10. The deer faced the **adversity** of an especially harsh winter. Deep snow covered all the grass and shrubs, so food was scarce.

    **A** collaboration        **B** confusion        **C** hardship        **D** interest

**Vocabulary in Context**

                                 Vocabulary in Context G7, SV 9780547625805

# Understanding Multiple-Meaning Words

The words in the box have more than one meaning. Look for clues in each sentence to tell which meaning is being used. Write the letter of the meaning next to the correct sentence.

---

**coordination**
a. the skillful action of muscles to do a complex movement or task
b. the act of getting different groups or people to work together

**sketch**
a. a drawing or an outline
b. a performance

---

_____ **1.** Juggling three balls at once requires great *coordination*.

_____ **2.** Many agencies are working in *coordination* to help the victims of the tragic earthquake.

_____ **3.** Our English class will rehearse a one-act *sketch* of a play this afternoon.

_____ **4.** The *sketch* Marco drew of the castle is very good.

# Find the Word

Read each sentence. Look for clues to help you complete each sentence with a word from the box. Write the word on the line.

---

| menace | obstacle | invigorating | feat | competence |

---

1. To complete the _____ course, the dog had to jump hurdles, weave around poles, and race through tunnels.

2. We couldn't believe Simone could hold his breath for one full minute; it was an amazing

   _____.

3. My little sister is such a _____; she constantly gets into my things.

4. The experienced doctor showed great _____ while performing surgery in unfavorable conditions.

5. The splash of cold water on my face was _____; I'm definitely awake now.

Word Skills

# Analogies

An **analogy** compares two pairs of words. The relationship between the first pair of words is the same as the relationship between the second pair of words.

Example: *Happy* is to *sad* as *rough* is to *smooth*.

Use the words in the box to complete the following analogies.

| obstacle | feats | support | menace | invigorating |
|---|---|---|---|---|

**1.** *Soft* is to *hard* as *boring* is to _____.

**2.** *Competitor* is to *player* as *handicap* is to _____.

**3.** *Quiet* is to *silent* as *tricks* is to _____.

**4.** *Danger* is to *hazard* as *pest* is to _____.

**5.** *Stamina* is to *endurance* as *assistance* is to _____.

# Rewriting Sentences

Rewrite each sentence using one of the words from the box.

| identity | acrobatics | coordination | sketch | competence |
|---|---|---|---|---|

**1.** The visiting team performed some amazing gymnastic tricks in the competition.

_____

**2.** Do you know the name of that team's top competitor?

_____

**3.** Julian shows ability on the basketball court; he rarely misses a shot.

_____

**4.** The architect drew a picture of what the building would look like.

_____

**5.** Playing three games in one day requires a great arrangement of schedules.

_____

# Synonym or Antonym?

Each numbered word below is either a synonym or an antonym of the underlined word in the sentence. Write *S* for synonym or *A* for antonym on each line.

The horned worm is a <u>menace</u> to our vegetable garden.

_____ **1.** pest

_____ **2.** aid

_____ **3.** threat

_____ **4.** nuisance

The tree limb that fell in the path proved to be an <u>obstacle</u> to the mountain bikers.

_____ **5.** interference

_____ **6.** advantage

_____ **7.** benefit

_____ **8.** help

The sailboat tour in the bay was <u>invigorating</u>—the wind and the salt air felt fantastic!

_____ **9.** energizing

_____ **10.** depressing

_____ **11.** discouraging

_____ **12.** stimulating

The performer's <u>feats</u> of magic stunned the audience.

_____ **13.** acts

_____ **14.** achievements

Beth's <u>coordination</u> allows her to learn the difficult dance steps.

_____ **15.** control

_____ **16.** clumsiness

_____ **17.** grace

_____ **18.** technique

The runner showed great <u>competence</u> by avoiding the hazards on the racecourse.

_____ **19.** incapability

_____ **20.** awkwardness

_____ **21.** inability

_____ **22.** skill

The fans showed <u>support</u> for their team by clapping and cheering.

_____ **23.** encouragement

_____ **24.** disapproval

_____ **25.** frustration

**Word Skills**

# Writing

Kitty O'Neil is a stuntwoman and a race-car driver. Tell about a career that involves adventure. What would you find exciting about this career?

Write a paragraph that identifies and discusses this adventurous career. Be sure to include details that describe the challenge this new career might present. Use some vocabulary words from this unit in your writing.

_____

_____

_____

_____

_____

_____

_____

_____

_____

_____

_____

_____

_____

Writing

# Underwater Explorer

Read the selection below. Think about the meanings of the **boldfaced** words. Then go back to the selection. Underline the words or sentences that give you a clue to the meaning of each **boldfaced** word.

---

Jacques Cousteau put on his new diving goggles and waded into the sea. The twenty-six-year-old Frenchman had enjoyed swimming ever since he was a boy. Now, as he dropped under the surface of the water, an entirely new world opened up. An **array** of fish, seaweed, and rocks appeared around him. Yet despite this colorful variety of sea life, he felt a sense of peace in this ocean world. At that moment, Jacques Cousteau decided to become a deep-sea explorer.

The year was 1936, and little was known about ocean diving. Diving equipment was dangerous, heavy, and bulky. Cousteau began working to make diving safer and easier. He started wearing rubber fins so he could swim faster underwater. Later he invented a breathing system that used tanks to carry oxygen. This system allowed divers to **inhale** and **exhale**, or breathe in and out, underwater.

Ten years later, Cousteau set up the Undersea Research Group with other divers who were exploring the deep sea. He and his **colleagues** explored shipwrecks. They also studied marine life.

In 1950, Cousteau realized one of his greatest ambitions. With the help of a wealthy friend, he bought a research ship, the *Calypso*. While exploring the oceans, divers on the *Calypso* often **confronted** sharks and other dangers. The **fearlessness** of the explorers became well known. Cousteau wrote several books about their experiences. He has produced many films about sea life. Three of the films won Academy Awards.

As Cousteau grew older, he spent more and more time fighting **environmental** problems. During his long diving career, he had seen that pollution killed ocean life by destroying the homes of many fish. In the 1960s and 1970s, his television series *The Undersea World of Jacques Cousteau* dramatized underwater exploration and concern for the health of the ocean. From his own experiences, Cousteau knew that **cooperation** is the key to success. People must work together to protect sea life.

Jacques Cousteau's accomplishments made him one of the **dominant** figures in the field of ocean study. This powerful position also made him an important **advisor** to a new generation of sea explorers. Even after his death, Jacques Cousteau's efforts live on. Today, his foundation continues his mission to preserve our world.

# Context Clues

Meanings for the vocabulary words are given below. Go back to the selection and read each sentence that contains a vocabulary word. If you still cannot tell the meaning, look for clues in the sentences that come before and after the one with the vocabulary word. Write each word in front of its meaning.

| array | advisor | dominant | confronted | colleagues |
|---|---|---|---|---|
| cooperation | environmental | fearlessness | inhale | exhale |

1. _____ : fellow members of a profession; co-workers

2. _____ : large assortment or collection

3. _____ : to breathe in air through the nose or mouth

4. _____ : the state of being very brave; unafraid

5. _____ : a person who offers advice or information on a particular subject

6. _____ : the act or process of working together with others to achieve a common goal

7. _____ : to breathe out air through the nose or mouth

8. _____ : most influential or powerful

9. _____ : having to do with the surroundings, with nature

10. _____ : came face-to-face with; faced boldly

# Challenge Yourself

1. Name two activities that require *cooperation*.

_____

2. Name two *environmental* problems in the United States today.

_____

# Cloze Paragraph

Use the words in the box to complete the passage. Then read the passage again to be sure it makes sense.

Vocabulary in Context

| array | advisor | dominant | confronted | colleagues |
|-------|---------|----------|------------|------------|
| cooperation | environmental | fearlessness | inhale | exhale |

My uncle and his friends started a diving club. Besides diving together, most of the members are also

business (1) _____. The club members began by trying to learn as much as possible

about diving. They hired a professional diver to give them instructions. This teacher would also be the

club's (2) _____ when the group began to plan diving trips.

The instruction started with learning how to use fins, tanks, and weights. The student divers spent

long hours in a swimming pool practicing with their scuba equipment. They learned the proper way to

(3) _____, or breathe in, and to (4) _____, or breathe out.

They learned special methods of (5) _____ that could be used if one diver needed

emergency help underwater.

After the club members learned the basic skills of diving, they went on their first deep-sea diving

trip. They (6) _____ problems that they had not faced during their training.

They met these challenges without hesitating, and their teacher congratulated them for the

(7) _____ they showed in the face of danger. They did well because they were

prepared and understood what to do in an emergency.

The divers were always delighted when they saw a great variety of sea life. On almost every trip, they

saw a vast (8) _____ of ocean plants and animals. In many cases, though, pollution

was affecting the sea. The divers were so upset by this (9) _____ problem that they

decided to devote some time to help solve it.

Club members invited a speaker from the Cousteau Society to tell them how they could help. They

wrote to government officials to express their concern about the welfare of the oceans. Diving had been

their (10) _____ interest at first. Now, like Jacques Cousteau, they were interested

in everything that had to do with the world of the sea.

# Word Game

The underlined letters in each sentence below are part of one of the vocabulary words. Use the underlined letters and the context of the sentence to determine the correct vocabulary word. Write the word on the line.

| array | advisor | dominant | confronted | colleagues |
|-------|---------|----------|------------|------------|
| cooperation | environmental | fearlessness | inhale | exhale |

_____  1. After the company dug the iron out of the mountain, they realized that they had destroyed the homes of many animals.

_____  2. He took a deep breath and noticed how sweet it smelled in the flowering orange grove.

_____  3. Jack, his two sisters, and his father worked together for a whole week build a new chicken coop that the fox couldn't get into.

_____  4. Our team had less time to practice this week because of bad wea⟋  ；, but we will play with confidence on Saturday anyway.

_____  5. My friend, Ray, and I like to walk together in the meadow,  ⟋ ch is filled with hundreds of colorful flowers and fascinating in⟍ ⟍s.

_____  6. The ad said they were looking for a person who could ⟋ ⟍nsel students who needed guidance.

_____  7. I do think it is important that the club leader be the person who has the most power and influence.

_____  8. The bus driver demanded that the angry riders come to the front of the bus and tell her face-to-face what they were upset about.

_____  9. Most of the people who work in my brother's office are also members of his bowling league.

_____  10. Hal has such a terrible cold that his chest rattles every time he breathes out.

Name _____ Date _____

# Word Maze

All the words in the list below are hidden in the maze. The words are arranged forward, backward, up, down, and diagonally. Put a circle around each word as you find it and cross the word off the list. Different words may overlap and use the same letter.

| array | advisor | dominant | confronted | colleagues |
|-------|---------|----------|------------|------------|
| cooperation | environmental | fearlessness | inhale | exhale |

C  K  N  O  I  T  A  R  E  P  O  O  C  A

O  U  E  C  J  E  K  F  N  J  Q  C  D  D

L  R  X  B  M  N  I  B  U  C  H  V  Y  L

L  F  H  V  D  V  Y  Y  I  V  I  K  V  K

E  D  A  N  O  I  B  P  I  S  B  B  N  J

A  E  L  B  G  R  C  P  O  N  X  T  W  L

G  T  E  P  I  O  B  R  W  I  H  N  I  Y

U  N  S  S  E  N  S  S  E  L  R  A  E  F

E  O  L  C  S  M  P  S  M  F  K  N  L  F

S  R  I  J  D  E  F  O  N  A  A  I  B  E

F  F  P  O  X  N  E  I  T  R  B  M  R  S

C  N  S  U  D  T  M  D  R  L  M  O  Z  O

X  O  D  X  X  A  U  A  R  U  A  D  O  O

M  C  L  T  O  L  Y  A  L  H  W  F  C  V

Name _____  Date _____

# Standardized Test Practice

Read the sentence. Think about the meaning of the boldfaced word and choose the word that best completes the sentence. Circle the letter of your choice.

**TIP**
This test will show you how well you understand the meaning of the words. Think about the meaning of the boldfaced word before you choose your answer.

1. An **array** of goods means that there are _____ to choose from.
   A many        C two
   B none        D few

2. A person who displays **fearlessness** is _____.
   A wise        C brave
   B afraid      D foolish

3. When someone has **confronted** a dangerous situation, he has _____ it.
   A avoided     C surprised
   B faced       D retrieved

4. When you work in **cooperation** with someone, you work _____ her.
   A against     C behind
   B without     D with

5. When you **inhale**, you breathe _____.
   A out         C under
   B heavy       D in

6. **Environmental** experts study the _____.
   A surroundings   C moon
   B disease        D construction

7. A **dominant** color will be the one you _____ most in a room.
   A scratch     C dislike
   B tempt       D notice

8. A clothing **advisor** would _____ clothes for you to wear.
   A fold        C guarantee
   B wash        D recommend

9. A teacher's **colleagues** are other _____.
   A students    C schools
   B teachers    D parents

10. When you **exhale**, you _____ your breath.
    A release    C excuse
    B accept     D count

Name _____ Date _____

# Find the Word

Read each sentence. Look for clues to help you complete each sentence with a word from the box. Write the word on the line.

| multitude | authority | prominent | defy |
| associate | valiant | pioneers | fearsome |

1. The crew members of *Apollo 11* were _____ in space travel; they were the first to land on the moon.

2. We were impressed by the _____ little kitten when she scared away the two dogs that were chasing her.

3. Let's ask the tour guide which trail to hike since he is an _____ on the area.

4. Her green eyes are striking; they are her most _____ feature.

5. Billy made a _____ face, hoping to scare his older sister.

6. That tropical bird shows a _____ of brilliant colors.

7. I will not _____ my mother's wishes; I will be home by dinnertime.

8. My mother and her _____ at work are collecting money for the community food bank.

# Writing Sentences

Write an original sentence with each of the words in the box.

| valiant | authority | associate |

1. _____

2. _____

3. _____

# Analogies

An **analogy** compares two pairs of words. The relationship between the first pair of words is the same as the relationship between the second pair of words.

Example: *Sweet* is to *sour* as *dark* is to *light*.

Use the words in the box to complete the following analogies.

| multitude | authority | prominent | defy | fearsome |
|---|---|---|---|---|

**1.** *Lawyer* is to *attorney* as *expert* is to _____.

**2.** *Skill* is to *talent* as *collection* is to _____.

**3.** *Criticized* is to *praised* as *obey* is to _____.

**4.** *Jump* is to *crouch* as *calming* is to _____.

**5.** *Mountain* is to *valley* as *invisible* is to _____.

# Sentence Completion

Read each sentence. Look for clues to help you complete each sentence with a word from the box. Write the word on the line.

| associate | pioneers | cooperation |
|---|---|---|

**1.** The flight attendant asked for the _____ of all of the passengers during the emergency landing.

**2.** The Wright brothers were _____ of aviation since they were the first to fly an airplane.

**3.** Jillian and her _____ in the accounting department will organize the company picnic.

Word Skills

# Rewriting Sentences

Rewrite each sentence using one of the words from the box.

| | | | | |
|---|---|---|---|---|
| multitude | authority | prominent | defy | associate |
| valiant | environmental | fearsome | inhale | exhale |

1. Did you know Mr. Wilcox is an expert on World War II?

   _____

2. The mountain range is a visible feature in the Colorado landscape.

   _____

3. Have you asked your business partner how she wants to handle the new company policies?

   _____

4. We saw a large collection of antique cars at the car show.

   _____

5. The building was designed to withstand a large earthquake.

   _____

6. The doctor asked Marta to blow air out slowly.

   _____

7. Breathe in quickly; then hold your breath.

   _____

8. The brave knight slayed the dragon and rescued the princess.

   _____

9. We read an article about the ecological impact of greenhouse gases.

   _____

10. The powerful winds of the hurricane tore through the parking lot, turning some cars over and carrying others yards away.

   _____

Word Skills

# Writing

Environmental issues have concerned Jacques Cousteau and others. What are some of the ways that people are harming Earth?

Write an editorial for a magazine that tells about one practice that is harming our environment. In your editorial, describe the practice. Explain why you believe the practice is or is not justified. Use some vocabulary words from this unit in your writing.

_____

_____

_____

_____

_____

_____

_____

_____

_____

_____

_____

_____

Writing

# Glossary

## A

| | | |
|---|---|---|
| **abnormal** | *adjective* | unusual; unnatural (page 28) |
| **ace** | *noun* | a person who is an expert in his or her field (page 88) |
| **acclaim** | *noun* | recognition or approval (page 68) |
| **accumulated** | *verb* | collected; piled up (page 28) |
| **acknowledge** | *verb* | to admit; recognize (page 18) |
| **acrobatics** | *noun* | stunts that require strength and good balance (page 88) |
| **actual** | *adjective* | real; true (page 18) |
| **acute** | *adjective* | extreme; difficult or severe (page 68) |
| **adverse** | *adjective* | difficult or unfavorable (page 68) |
| **adversity** | *noun* | trouble or difficulty (page 88) |
| **advisor** | *noun* | a person who gives advice (page 98) |
| **aggressive** | *adjective* | bold; forceful (page 68) |
| **agility** | *noun* | the ability to move quickly and easily (page 88) |
| **agonizing** | *adjective* | causing great pain or suffering (page 68) |
| **alter** | *verb* | to make different; modify (page 9) |
| **antics** | *noun* | stunts or tricks (page 88) |
| **apparel** | *noun* | clothing (page 49) |
| **aptitude** | *noun* | natural ability or talent (page 68) |
| **array** | *noun* | variety; large collection (page 98) |
| **assurance** | *noun* | confidence; a guarantee or promise (page 88) |
| **attitude** | *noun* | point of view; way of thinking (page 38) |
| **audible** | *adjective* | able to be heard (page 78) |
| **awareness** | *noun* | knowledge; realization (page 23) |

## B

| | | |
|---|---|---|
| **bewildering** | *adjective* | causing confusion (page 64) |
| **bewitch** | *verb* | to attract as if by the power of witchcraft or magic; cast a spell on (page 48) |
| **bitterness** | *noun* | feelings of resentment and ill will (page 58) |

## C

| | | |
|---|---|---|
| **characters** | *noun* | symbols that stand for an object, idea, or sound (page 64) |
| **chemist** | *noun* | an expert in chemistry (page 8) |
| **civic** | *adjective* | of or relating to a citizen, citizenship, or governmental affairs (page 39); *Related word:* **civilian** (page 44) |
| **cluster** | *noun* | a number of things or persons gathered together; a bunch (page 28) |

| | | |
|---|---|---|
| **colleagues** | *noun* | fellow workers (page 98) |
| **compelled** | *verb* | forced (page 48) |
| **competitors** | *noun* | people who strive for an object, prize, or position; rivals (page 49) |
| **concern** | *noun* | special interest or regard arising through a personal tie or relationship; a worry (page 38) |
| **conditions** | *noun* | manners or states of being; states of health; social ranks; things called for as a requirement (page 8) |
| **conducted** | *verb* | carried on; managed; led (page 8) |
| **confronted** | *verb* | faced; stood up to (page 98) |
| **considerable** | *adjective* | worth thinking about; important; much or large (page 48) |
| **contour** | *noun* | the outline, edge, or shape (page 78) |
| **contradicts** | *verb* | resists or opposes an argument; denies the truth of (page 49) |
| **cooperation** | *noun* | the act or state of working together (page 98) |
| **coordination** | *noun* | smooth and skillful body movements (page 88) |
| **crucial** | *adjective* | critically important (page 78) |
| **cultured** | *adjective* | refined; educated; knowledgeable about literary and artistic works (page 38) |
| **curious** | *adjective* | questioning; eager for information (page 28) |

## D

| | | |
|---|---|---|
| **decrease** | *verb* | to lessen; diminish (page 48) |
| **dedication** | *noun* | wholehearted devotion; commitment (page 38) |
| **desperate** | *adjective* | extremely dangerous or serious; hopeless (page 28) |
| **destructive** | *adjective* | causing great damage (page 78) |
| **detect** | *verb* | to discover the existence or presence of (page 8) |
| **determination** | *noun* | act of deciding firmly and purposefully; resolve (page 38) |
| **development** | *noun* | growth; an event or happening (page 8) |
| **dialects** | *noun* | forms of speech spoken in a certain area (page 64) |
| **disability** | *noun* | a lack of ability to do a certain thing (page 88) |
| **discipline** | *noun* | training that develops self-control or orderliness; the result of such training (page 38) |
| **disclose** | *verb* | to bring into view; uncover; make known (page 18) |
| **dishearten** | *verb* | to discourage someone or make someone lose heart (page 68) |
| **disrupts** | *verb* | breaks or interrupts (page 78) |
| **dominant** | *adjective* | most powerful; ruling (page 98) |
| **doused** | *verb* | poured liquid over; drenched (page 18) |

Vocabulary in Context G7, SV 9780547625805

## E

| | | |
|---|---|---|
| **effectiveness** | *noun* | usefulness; forcefulness (page 29) |
| **endeared** | *verb* | made beloved (page 28) |
| **endeavors** | *noun* | serious efforts or undertakings (page 38) |
| **enforced** | *verb* | carried out effectively; strengthened (page 39) |
| **ensures** | *verb* | makes certain by taking necessary precautions; guarantees (page 49) |
| **environmental** | *adjective* | having to do with the surroundings in which things live (page 98) |
| **establish** | *verb* | to start; organize (page 8) |
| **eventful** | *adjective* | filled with important happenings (page 58) |
| **excel** | *verb* | to do something very well; outdo (page 68) |
| **excluding** | *adjective* | leaving out (page 64) |
| **exert** | *verb* | to put into action; use force (page 78) |
| **exhale** | *verb* | to breathe out (page 98) |
| **exhilarating** | *adjective* | thrilling or stimulating (page 88) |

## F

| | | |
|---|---|---|
| **fearlessness** | *noun* | lack of fear (page 98) |
| **figurative** | *adjective* | not literal (page 64) |
| **florist** | *noun* | one who sells flowers (page 8) |
| **formations** | *noun* | things formed; the ways in which some things are arranged; structures (page 8) |
| **frequently** | *adverb* | often; usually (page 8) |
| **friction** | *noun* | the heat and strain caused when surfaces rub together (page 78) |

## G

| | | |
|---|---|---|
| **guarantee** | *noun* | a promise regarding the satisfactory performance of a product or satisfactory outcome of an event; a pledge (page 8) |

## H

| | | |
|---|---|---|
| **handicap** | *noun* | a disability or limitation (page 8) |
| **haven** | *noun* | a place of shelter or safety (page 49) |
| **hazardous** | *adjective* | dangerous; risky (page 18) |
| **hemisphere** | *noun* | one half of the globe (page 78) |
| **hinder** | *verb* | to hold back; slow the progress of (page 18) |

## I

| | | |
|---|---|---|
| **identical** | *adjective* | exactly alike (page 64) |
| **identity** | *noun* | all the things that make a specific person different from others (page 88) |

| | | |
|---|---|---|
| **ignited** | *verb* | excited feelings for; set afire (page 38) |
| **immeasurable** | *adjective* | too great to be measured (page 58) |
| **imposing** | *verb* | forcing upon (page 64) |
| **impractical** | *adjective* | not useful or efficient (page 64) |
| **impure** | *adjective* | improper; unclean; dirty (page 18); *Related word:* **impurity** (page 23) |
| **informative** | *adjective* | instructive; educational (page 9) |
| **inhale** | *verb* | to breathe in (page 98) |
| **inseparable** | *adjective* | unable to be parted; joined very closely (page 8) |
| **intrigue** | *noun* | secret plot; conspiracy (page 18) |
| **inviting** | *adjective* | appealing; tempting (page 18) |
| **isolated** | *adjective* | set apart from others (page 49) |

## J

| | | |
|---|---|---|
| **journalist** | *noun* | a person who reports or edits news for a newscast or newspaper or other form of media (page 18) |

## L

| | | |
|---|---|---|
| **legitimate** | *adjective* | reasonable; justifiable; genuine (page 38) |
| **lingering** | *verb* | being slow in leaving; delaying (page 18) |
| **literal** | *adjective* | basic; factual and exact (page 64) |
| **loathe** | *verb* | to dislike strongly; hate (page 48) |
| **lodge** | *verb* | to occupy a place temporarily; come to rest and remain firmly fixed (page 49) |

## M

| | | |
|---|---|---|
| **magnificent** | *adjective* | splendid; extremely impressive (page 9) |
| **maneuvered** | *verb* | schemed or plotted; moved in a controlled manner (page 18) |
| **marathon** | *noun* | an extremely long race or contest (page 68) |
| **metropolitan** | *adjective* | relating to a central city and its surrounding communities (page 18) |
| **mission** | *noun* | the special duty that a person or group is sent to do; a group of persons sent by a church or government to perform a special duty (page 28) |
| **mobile** | *adjective* | capable of movement or of being moved (page 49) |
| **mute** | *adjective* | silent; unable to speak (page 29) |
| **mutiny** | *noun* | a revolt against authority, especially by soldiers or sailors against their officers (page 28) |

## O

| | | |
|---|---|---|
| **obligation** | *noun* | duty; commitment (page 39); *Related word*: **obligate** (page 44) |

| | | |
|---|---|---|
| **observe** | *verb* | to look at closely; examine; watch (page 8) |
| **outburst** | *noun* | a sudden, violent act or exclamation (page 59) |

**P**

| | | |
|---|---|---|
| **passionate** | *adjective* | showing or feeling strong emotion (page 58) |
| **persevered** | *verb* | continued in some effort or course of action in spite of difficulty; persisted (page 38) |
| **policy** | *noun* | a principle that guides action; definite course or plan of action (page 39) |
| **politics** | *noun* | the art or science of government; governmental actions or practices (page 38) |
| **prediction** | *noun* | a statement of what one thinks will happen (page 8) |
| **proclaim** | *verb* | to show; announce; state publicly (page 49) |
| **pursuit** | *noun* | the act of chasing or seeking (page 18) |

**Q**

| | | |
|---|---|---|
| **quest** | *noun* | a search or journey (page 28) |

**R**

| | | |
|---|---|---|
| **reform** | *noun* | removal or correction of faults or errors (page 38) |
| **reliable** | *adjective* | dependable (page 18) |
| **render** | *verb* | to deliver; to present (page 9) |
| **repentance** | *noun* | deep regret or remorse for something one has done (page 59) |
| **repulsive** | *adjective* | disgusting; upsetting (page 29) |
| **resent** | *verb* | to feel or show bitter hurt or anger toward someone (page 49) |
| **respect** | *noun* | high or special regard (page 38) |

**S**

| | | |
|---|---|---|
| **safeguard** | *verb* | to protect against; keep secure (page 9) |
| **seasonal** | *adjective* | dependent upon the seasons or time of year (page 9) |
| **sentiment** | *noun* | feeling or emotion (page 59) |
| **severity** | *noun* | harshness; intensity (page 78) |
| **signify** | *verb* | to stand for; to represent (page 64) |
| **skirmish** | *noun* | a minor dispute between opposing forces; a minor fight (page 49) |
| **social** | *adjective* | of or relating to human communities (page 38) |
| **solemn** | *adjective* | serious; deeply earnest (page 18) |
| **stamina** | *noun* | strength and endurance (page 68) |
| **suspense** | *noun* | mental uncertainty; state of excitement regarding the outcome of an event (page 28) |

Vocabulary in Context G7, SV 9780547625805

## T

| | | |
|---|---|---|
| **tangible** | *adjective* | able to be touched (page 58) |
| **technician** | *noun* | one having special scientific or mechanical skills (page 28) |
| **testimony** | *noun* | any form of evidence; a statement made by a witness under oath in a court of law (page 28) |
| **toxic** | *adjective* | poisonous (page 49) |
| **transformation** | *noun* | change in shape, size, appearance, or character (page 29) |
| **transmitted** | *verb* | sent; transferred (page 48) |
| **tremor** | *noun* | a shaking, rolling motion (page 78) |
| **tussle** | *noun* | a struggle; a small fight (page 59) |

## U

| | | |
|---|---|---|
| **unaccountable** | *adjective* | not responsible for; unexplainable (page 18) |
| **unaware** | *adjective* | unknowing; not conscious of (page 18) |
| **uncomprehending** | *adjective* | not understanding (page 58) |
| **upheld** | *verb* | gave support to, especially emotional support (page 39) |
| **untimely** | *adjective* | occurring at the wrong time (page 29) |

## V

| | | |
|---|---|---|
| **venture** | *noun* | a risky undertaking, particularly in a business or financial sense (page 28) |
| **versions** | *noun* | descriptions or retellings related from one person's point of view; interpretations (page 18) |
| **versus** | *preposition* | against (page 39) |
| **veterans** | *noun* | people with long experience in a particular field (page 49) |
| **violate** | *verb* | to break or disregard; treat with disrespect (page 49) |
| **vital** | *adjective* | essential; necessary; full of life (page 29) |
| **vivid** | *adjective* | lively; bright; lifelike (page 18) |

## Z

| | | |
|---|---|---|
| **zeal** | *noun* | enthusiasm (page 28) |

# Answer Key

## Pages 10–11

1. D
2. D
3. C
4. B
5. D
6. A
7. C
8. A
9. A
10. B
11. C
12. D
13. A
14. B
15. C
16. A
17. B
18. A
19. B
20. D

## Page 12

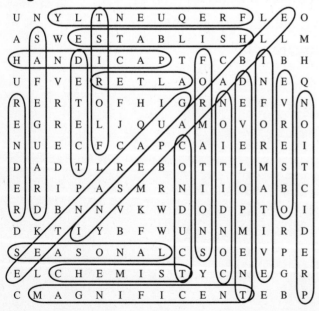

## Page 13

1. C
2. A
3. A
4. D
5. C
6. D
7. C
8. C
9. B
10. D

## Page 14

1. florist; floral
2. frequently; frequency
3. conducted; conductor
4. handicapped; handicap
5. observe; observation
6. alterations; alter
7. detector; detect
8. development, develop
9. magnify; magnificent
10. reestablish; establish

## Page 15

1. chemist
2. flora
3. observation
4. separate
5. conductor
6. rendered
7. magnificent
8. infrequently
9. season
10. develop

Vocabulary in Context G7, SV 9780547625805

**Page 16**

**The Prefix *un-***

1. D
2. A
3. C
4. E
5. B

**The Suffix *-ion***

1. C
2. E
3. A
4. B
5. D

**The Latin Root *magni***

1. magnify
2. magnificence
3. magnify
4. magnify
5. magnificence

**Page 17**

Answers will vary.

**Pages 19–20**

1. A
2. D
3. D
4. B
5. B
6. B
7. B
8. A
9. A
10. D
11. D
12. B

13. C
14. D
15. C
16. A
17. C
18. B
19. D
20. A

**Page 21**

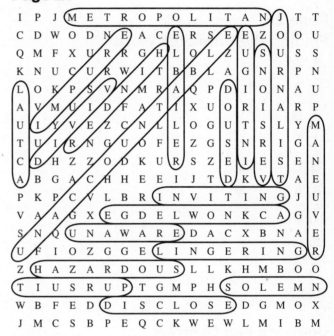

**Page 22**

1. B
2. B
3. A
4. C
5. C
6. D
7. C
8. A
9. D
10. D

**Page 23–24**

1. A

Vocabulary in Context G7, SV 9780547625805

2. B
3. B
4. B
5. C
6. B
7. B
8. B
9. B
10. C

## Page 25
### Finding the Unrelated Word
1. C
2. B
3. D
4. D
5. C
6. A
7. D
8. C
9. B
10. C

### Compare and Contrast
Answers will vary. Possible responses:

1. speaking vividly is more lively.
2. both have a sense of knowing.
3. you can express your feelings in both.
4. solemnness is more serious.
5. a hazard has a degree of danger.

## Page 26
Answers will vary. Possible responses:

1. unreliable: not reliable; not able to be depended on
2. uninviting: not inviting; not appealing
3. immature: childish; not mature
4. unsuitable: not appropriate; not suitable
5. immovable: stationary; not movable

## Page 27
Answers will vary.

## Page 30
1. A
2. D
3. B

## Pages 31–32
1. C
2. B
3. A
4. D
5. A
6. A
7. C
8. B
9. C
10. C
11. A
12. C
13. B
14. B
15. B
16. B
17. D
18. B
19. A
20. B

## Page 33
### Across
2. endeared
4. mutiny
5. repulsive
6. mute

Vocabulary in Context G7, SV 9780547625805

**7.** technician

**10.** abnormal

**11.** curious

**13.** venture

**14.** testimony

**16.** effectiveness

## Down

**1.** quest

**3.** desperate

**4.** mission

**8.** cluster

**9.** accumulated

**12.** suspense

**13.** vital

**15.** zeal

## Page 34

**1.** D

**2.** C

**3.** C

**4.** D

**5.** C

**6.** C

**7.** A

**8.** A

**9.** D

**10.** B

## Page 35

**1.** B

**2.** C

**3.** A

**4.** A

**5.** B

**6.** A

**7.** B

## Page 36

### True-False

**1.** F

**2.** F

**3.** T

**4.** T

**5.** F

**6.** F

**7.** F

**8.** F

**9.** F

**10.** T

### Finding the Unrelated Word

**1.** D

**2.** C

**3.** A

**4.** D

**5.** C

**6.** C

## Page 37

Answers will vary.

## Pages 40–41

**1.** B

**2.** C

**3.** D

**4.** B

**5.** A

**6.** C

**7.** D

**8.** C

**9.** C

**10.** C

**11.** A

**12.** B

**13.** B

Vocabulary in Context G7, SV 9780547625805

**14.** D

**15.** D

**16.** A

**17.** B

**18.** A

**19.** D

**20.** A

## Page 42

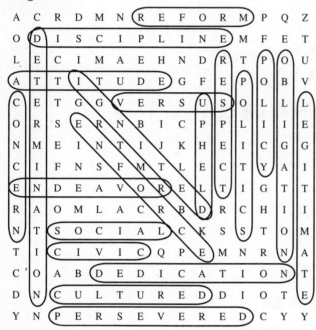

## Page 43

**1.** D

**2.** C

**3.** A

**4.** B

**5.** A

**6.** A

**7.** C

**8.** A

**9.** B

**10.** D

## Page 44

Answers will vary. Possible responses:

**1.** *enforcement*: ensuring obedience

**2.** *obligate*: force or compel

**3.** *respectable*: satisfactory, but not exceptional

**4.** *socialize*: to mingle in a friendly manner

**5.** *inform*: tell or make aware

**6.** *culture*: traits and habits of a particular society

**7.** *civilian*: a person who is not in the military or law enforcement

**8.** *society*: a group of humans brought together by common culture

**9.** *respectful*: showing honor or respect for someone or something

## Page 45
### True-False

**1.** T

**2.** F

**3.** F

**4.** T

**5.** T

**6.** T

**7.** F

**8.** T

**9.** F

**10.** T

### Challenge Yourself

Answers will vary. Suggested responses are provided.

**1.** school, Scouts

**2.** tortillas, celebrations with music

**3.** excited, hopeful

## Page 46

**1.** inform

**2.** conform

**3.** deformed

**4.** transform

5. conform

6. formulate

7. uniform

8. perform

9. information

10. transform

11. deformed

12. perform

13. uniform

## Page 47

Answers will vary.

## Pages 50–51

1. B

2. A

3. C

4. A

5. D

6. C

7. B

8. A

9. C

10. B

11. A

12. A

13. B

14. D

15. C

16. B

17. C

18. B

19. D

20. C

## Page 52

1. skirmish

2. violate

3. apparel

4. veterans

5. transmitted

6. compelled

7. toxic

8. proclaim

9. bewitch

10. mobile

11. competitors

12. loathe

13. contradicts

14. lodge

15. decrease

16. ensures

17. haven

18. isolated

19. considerable

20. resent

## Page 53

1. C

2. A

3. A

4. B

5. C

6. B

7. A

8. C

9. B

## Page 54

1. B

2. D

3. C

4. D

5. D

6. A

7. C

Vocabulary in Context G7, SV 9780547625805

8. B

9. C

10. D

**Page 55**

1. F

2. T

3. F

4. T

5. F

6. F

7. F

8. F

9. T

10. T

11. F

12. T

13. T

14. F

15. T

**Page 56**

1. proclamation

2. claim

3. exclaimed

4. exclamation

5. clamor

6. claim

7. proclamation

8. clamor

9. exclaimed

10. exclamation

**Page 57**

Answers will vary.

**Page 60**

1. immeasurable

2. eventful

3. bitterness

4. passionate

5. tussle

6. uncomprehending

7. outburst

8. tangible

9. repentance

10. sentiment

**Page 61**

**Page 62**
**Cloze Paragraph**

1. outburst

2. uncomprehending

3. sentiment

4. bitterness

5. passionate

6. immeasurable

7. tangible

8. tussle

9. eventful

10. repentance

Vocabulary in Context G7, SV 9780547625805

## Challenge Yourself

Answers will vary. Suggested responses are provided.

1. swimming, going to college
2. arguments between brother and sister, arguments between sports teams
3. someone does not tell the truth, someone cheats on a test

## Page 63

1. C
2. A
3. B
4. C
5. C
6. C
7. B
8. A
9. D
10. C

## Page 64

1. figurative
2. bewildering
3. characters
4. literal
5. dialects
6. impractical
7. signify
8. Excluding
9. imposing
10. identical

## Page 65
### Word Origins

1. dialects
2. identical
3. bewildering

4. signify
5. literal
6. impractical
7. figurative
8. characters

## Understanding Multiple-Meaning Words

1. b
2. d
3. c
4. a

## Page 66

1. uncomprehending; not understanding
2. impractical; not useful or efficient
3. immeasurable; too great to be measured
4. unaware; unknowing, not conscious of
5. uncommon; unusual, remarkable, exceptional
6. improbable; unlikely
7. unmindful; unaware, careless
8. immovable; cannot be moved, firmly fixed

## Page 67

Answers will vary.

## Page 69
### Context Clues

1. marathon
2. aptitude
3. excel
4. stamina
5. acclaim
6. adverse
7. acute
8. dishearten
9. agonizing
10. aggressive

## Challenge Yourself

Answers will vary. Suggested responses are provided.

1. running, football
2. poverty, hunger
3. a poor grade, not being chosen for the debate team
4. sports, playing an instrument

## Page 70
### Across

1. stamina
4. excel
5. marathon
7. adverse
8. agonizing
9. dishearten
10. acute

### Down

2. acclaim
3. aggressive
6. aptitude

## Page 71
### Word Origins

1. excel
2. acute
3. agonizing
4. aptitude
5. adverse
6. aggressive
7. acclaim

### Connotations

1. stamina
2. aggressive
3. marathon
4. dishearten

5. acclaim

## Page 72
### Word Groups

1. adverse
2. aptitude
3. excel
4. aggressive
5. stamina
6. acute
7. dishearten
8. acclaim
9. marathon

### Antonyms

1. acute
2. dishearten
3. agonizing
4. aggressive
5. excel
6. acclaim
7. stamina
8. adverse

## Page 73

1. B
2. C
3. B
4. D
5. A
6. A
7. D
8. C
9. A
10. B

## Page 74
### Analogies

1. acute

2. frustrate

3. marathon

4. aptitude

5. aggression

**Find the Word**

1. acclamation

2. excellence

3. avert

4. agony

5. tenacity

**Page 75**

Definitions will vary.

**Page 76**

1. S
2. A
3. S
4. A
5. S
6. S
7. S
8. S
9. A
10. A
11. S
12. A
13. S
14. A
15. S
16. S
17. A
18. A
19. S
20. A

**Page 77**

Answers will vary.

**Page 79**

1. friction

2. audible

3. contour

4. tremor

5. severity

6. disrupts

7. crucial

8. destructive

9. hemisphere

10. exert

**Page 80**

**Page 81**
**Find the Word**

1. hemisphere

2. destructive

3. severity

4. friction

5. audible

6. crucial

7. contour

Vocabulary in Context G7, SV 9780547625805

8. tremor

9. disrupts

10. exert

**Challenge Yourself**

Answers will vary. Suggested answers are provided.

1. tsunami, earthquake

2. tornado, hail

**Page 82**

1. tremor

2. audible

3. severity

4. hemisphere

5. crucial

6. exert

7. destructive

8. contour

9. friction

10. disrupted

**Page 83**
**Rewriting Sentences**

1. This hemisphere has active earthquake areas.

2. An earthquake can change the contour of a shore.

3. We felt the first tremor.

4. The friction of the giant plates was building rapidly.

5. The plates exert pressure on one another.

**Connotations**

1. destructive

2. severity

3. crucial

4. disrupts

**Page 84**

1. C

2. D

3. A

4. D

5. C

6. B

7. A

8. C

9. D

10. B

**Page 85**
**Word Descriptions**

1. biosphere

2. essential

3. auditory

4. tsunami

5. structure

6. frayed

**Word Origins**

1. auditory

2. biosphere

3. structure

4. frayed

**Page 86**

1. intensity

2. biosphere

3. disrupts

4. frayed

5. structure

6. audible

7. stern

8. crucial

9. tsunami

10. contour

Vocabulary in Context G7, SV 9780547625805

## Page 87
Answers will vary.

## Page 89
1. disability
2. acrobatics
3. identity
4. coordination (or agility)
5. agility (or coordination)
6. assurance
7. adversity
8. ace
9. antics
10. exhilarating

## Page 90
What Stunt Performers Do: acrobatics; antics; additional answers will vary

Qualities of Stunt Performers: coordination; agility; additional answers will vary

Terms That Describe Stunt Performers: ace; additional answers will vary

How Audiences Might Describe Stunt Performances: exhilarating; additional answers will vary

## Page 91
### Across
1. identity
3. ace
5. disability
6. acrobatics
8. coordination
9. antics

### Down
2. exhilarating

3. assurance
4. adversity
7. agility

## Page 92
### Connotations
1. ace
2. adversity
3. antics
4. acrobatics
5. exhilarating
6. identity

## Word Pairs
Answers will vary.

## Page 93
1. C
2. A
3. A
4. B
5. D
6. C
7. C
8. A
9. D
10. C

## Page 94
### Understanding Multiple-Meaning Words
1. a
2. b
3. b
4. a

## Find the Word
1. obstacle
2. feat
3. menace

4. competence

5. invigorating

## Page 95
## Analogies

1. invigorating

2. obstacle

3. feats

4. menace

5. support

### Rewriting Sentences

Sentences will vary. Possible responses:

1. The visiting team performed some amazing acrobatics in the competition.

2. Do you know the identity of that team's top competitor?

3. Julian shows competence on the basketball court; he rarely misses a shot.

4. The architect drew a sketch of what the building would look like.

5. Playing three games in one day requires a great coordination of schedules.

## Page 96

1. S

2. A

3. S

4. S

5. S

6. A

7. A

8. A

9. S

10. A

11. A

12. S

13. S

14. S

15. S

16. A

17. S

18. S

19. A

20. A

21. A

22. S

23. S

24. A

25. A

## Page 97
Answers will vary.

## Page 99
## Context Clues

1. colleagues

2. array

3. inhale

4. fearlessness

5. advisor

6. cooperation

7. exhale

8. dominant

9. environmental

10. confronted

### Challenge Yourself

Answers will vary. Suggested responses are provided.

1. being in a play, playing in an orchestra

2. air pollution, water pollution

## Page 100

1. colleagues

2. advisor

3. inhale

Vocabulary in Context G7, SV 9780547625805

**4.** exhale

**5.** cooperation

**6.** confronted

**7.** fearlessness

**8.** array

**9.** environmental

**10.** dominant

## Page 101

**1.** environmental

**2.** inhale

**3.** cooperation

**4.** fearlessness

**5.** array

**6.** advisor

**7.** dominant

**8.** confronted

**9.** colleagues

**10.** exhale

## Page 102

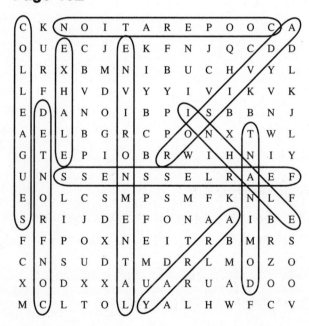

## Page 103

**1.** A

**2.** C

**3.** B

**4.** D

**5.** D

**6.** A

**7.** D

**8.** D

**9.** B

**10.** A

## Page 104
### Find the Word

**1.** pioneers

**2.** valiant

**3.** authority

**4.** prominent

**5.** fearsome

**6.** multitude

**7.** defy

**8.** associate

### Writing Sentences

Answers will vary.

## Page 105
### Analogies

**1.** authority

**2.** multitude

**3.** defy

**4.** fearsome

**5.** prominent

### Sentence Completion

**1.** cooperation

**2.** pioneers

**3.** associate

## Page 106

Answers will vary. Possible responses:

Answer Key
Vocabulary in Context G7, SV 9780547625805

1. Did you know Mr. Wilcox is an <u>authority</u> on World War II?

2. The mountain range is a <u>prominent</u> feature in the Colorado landscape.

3. Have you asked your <u>associate</u> how she wants to handle the new company policies?

4. We saw a <u>multitude</u> of antique cars at the car show.

5. The building was designed to <u>defy</u> a large earthquake.

6. The doctor asked Marta to <u>exhale</u> slowly.

7. <u>Inhale</u> quickly; then hold your breath.

8. The <u>valiant</u> knight slayed the dragon and rescued the princess.

9. We read an article about the <u>environmental</u> impact of greenhouse gases.

10. The <u>fearsome</u> winds of the hurricane tore through the parking lot, turning some cars over and carrying others yards away.

## Page 107

Answers will vary.